the seven pillars of partnering

PREFACE AND ACKNOWLEDGEMENTS

This report describes current best practice in Partnering in the UK building industry. It is based on the authors' ongoing research which was supported from 1994 to 1997 by the Engineering and Physical Sciences Research Council (EPSRC) and subsequently by a John Carlisle Scholarship. Best practice was identified and turned into practical guidance for designers and managers with the help of a series of seven meetings and workshops throughout 1997/98 with the Reading Construction Forum Partnering Task Force, chaired by Charles Johnston.

The report provides a companion to *Trusting the Team* by the same authors also working with the Reading Construction Forum Partnering Task Force. The earlier report has become firmly established as the basis of the UK building industry's approach to Partnering.

The authors would like to thank the following people and organisations for their help in compiling this report: all the Task Force members, especially Peter Shaw (who wrote Chapter 6) and the Chairman, Charles Johnston for his clear direction and commitment to the report; all the people who provided information for the case studies and Ian Ingram who assisted with the research into the benefits and costs of Partnering. We would also like to thank The John Carlisle Partnership, who provided a scholarship for The University of Reading to support Partnering research, and Paul Townsend and Mike Walters, Directors of the Reading Construction Forum, who have both helped with advice and practical support.

Published by Thomas Telford Publishing,
Thomas Telford Services Ltd,
1 Heron Quay,
London E14 4JD.

Copyright © Reading Construction Forum Ltd
April 1998.

The report was edited and designed by Camargue (Cheltenham) and printed by Thamesdown Colour.

ISBN 0-7277-2690-0

British Library Cataloguing-in-Publication Data.
A catalogue record for this book is available from the British Library.

Contents

HOW TO READ THE REPORT

SENIOR MANAGERS SHOULD READ:

- Chapters 1 and 2 to learn how Partnering is being used and the benefits it delivers.
- Chapter 6 to learn how Partnering is likely to develop in the future.

MANAGERS RESPONSIBLE FOR APPLYING PARTNERING SHOULD READ:

- Chapters 1 and 2 to get a quick overview.
- One or two of the journeys in Chapter 3.
- Chapter 4 brings the principles from all the research together. Initially read just the sub-headings to get a sense of the Seven Pillars.
- Chapter 5 initially use the checklists to help decide which pillars to work on; subsequently the checklists are a guide for project teams.
- Once you have decided which pillars to work on, read the detailed description in Chapter 4 for those pillars.
- Chapter 7 for background notes on legal and contractual issues.

Foreword

We are beginning to understand how we can achieve continuous improvement in the design and delivery of our construction projects through partnerships between the construction industry and its clients.

Partnering enables the industry to understand more clearly its clients' needs and objectives. It gives clients direct access to the hard-won knowledge and expertise of suppliers, constructors and designers. And partnering empowers all of us to develop our skills and apply them productively in the project process.

But, as the Seven Pillars of Partnering makes clear, partnering is hard work because it makes all of us accountable to each other for improving our performance. It encourages us to work together to solve problems and drive out waste in our processes.

The Seven Pillars of Partnering is a practical guide to best practices in partnering. It gives useful examples of improvements that have been delivered on real projects. And it gives an insight into the world of continous improvement that opens up as partnerships develop into strategic alliances. The Reading Construction Forum Partnering Task Force is to be congratulated on an excellent publication.

SIR NIGEL MOBBS

The Reading Construction Forum

The Reading Construction Forum is based at the University of Reading. It has close links with the Department of Construction Management & Engineering but is independent of the University and regularly commissions research from other institutions such as the University of the West of England at Bristol.

Members of the Forum are major companies concerned with achieving high quality in the design, construction and use of commercial, retail and industrial buildings. All are committed to change and innovation in the British and European building industries.

To achieve effective action the Forum is led by Principal Members who are drawn from international customers and building industry consultants, contractors and manufacturers. They work with leading researchers to identify specific actions needed to improve the performance of the UK building industry. However, to ensure that new ideas and best practice are applied widely, the Forum includes, as Members, organisations with varying levels of experience that want to take practical actions aimed at achieving high quality in building.

The over-riding purpose of the Forum is to enlist the active involvement of members in identifying, debating and activating the objectives.

The objectives are designed to achieve change by collaborative involvement rather than by perpetuating the confrontational aspects of the industry that historically have damaged its performance. To these ends the objectives of the Forum are:

- To provide a forum for members about all issues affecting quality, efficiency and innovation in the design, construction and use of commercial and industrial buildings.

- To identify the need for specific changes.

- To ensure that good practice which unites the industry in the interests of customers is widely disseminated.

- To encourage the research and development needed to ensure that the changes are effective and beneficial.

- To take practical actions aimed at improving the international competitiveness of the building industries in Britain and Europe, including helping to improve relationships between the industry and Government.

- To implement the results of research by the Reading Construction Forum and others.

- To work closely with other organisations committed to changing the construction industry for the better.

THE FORUM CONSISTS OF THE FOLLOWING COMPANIES

PRINCIPAL MEMBERS

Bovis Europe
Building Design Partnership
Roger Bullivant
Drake & Scull
Gardiner & Theobald
John Laing
John Lewis Partnership
O'Rourke Group
Richard Rogers Partnership
ROM
Sainsbury's
Slough Estates
Stanhope
Tarmac
Waterman Partnership

MEMBERS

Andover Controls
B&Q
Barclays Property Holdings
Birse Construction
Bucknall Group
Coverite
Ernest Green & Partners
Galliford (UK)
Gleeds
M J Gleeson Group
Hochtief
Irvine Whitlock
Kyle Stewart
Land Securities
Lovell Construction
Mansell
John Mowlem Construction
Nabarro Nathanson
Otis
R G Construction Management
Shepherd Construction
SmithKline Beecham
Stent Foundations
Taylor Joynson Garrett
Tesco Stores
Try Construction
Union Railways
Wates Integra

THE MEMBERS OF THE READING CONSTRUCTION FORUM PARTNERING TASK FORCE THAT HELPED PRODUCE THIS REPORT WERE:-

John Bennett	The University of Reading
Ian Beveridge	ROM
John Chadwick	RG Construction Management
Laurie Chetwood	Chetwood Associates
Terry Day	Laing South East
Paul Dewick	Irvine Whitlock
Peter Emerson	Rowen Structures
Shonagh Hay	Tarmac Professional Services
Sarah Jayes	The University of Reading
Charles Johnston (Chairman)	Sainsbury's
John Murphy	Bovis [now with CSB]
Tony Pressley	Lovell Construction
Peter Shaw	Taylor Joynson Garrett
Martin Sykes	BAA plc [now with PMMS Consulting]
Mike Thomas	Whitbread
Paul Townsend	Reading Construction Forum
Mike Walters	Reading Construction Forum

Executive Summary

- Partnering is a set of strategic actions that deliver vast improvements in construction performance. It is driven by a clear understanding of mutual objectives and cooperative decision making by a number of firms, who are all focused on using feedback to continuously improve their joint performance.

- Extensive research into the leading firms involved shows that the approach explained in the Reading Construction Forum's first report, *Trusting the Team* was merely a 'first generation' of Partnering.

- A 'second generation' of Partnering has now emerged that requires a strategic decision to cooperate in improving joint performance by a client and a group of consultants, contractors and specialists engaged in an ongoing series of projects. Second Generation Partnering is underpinned by 'Seven Pillars'.

- Each pillar represents a set of management actions that provide an essential element of Second Generation Partnering. The pillars are used strategically by strategic teams and on individual projects by project core teams.

- Second Generation Partnering is tough but those firms who have all Seven Pillars in place find that cost savings of 40% are not uncommon, and time savings of more than 50% are achievable.

- The research also identifies the beginnings of a third generation of Partnering in which the construction industry becomes a truly modern industry producing and marketing a range of products and services that clients are eager to invest in.

- The resulting Third Generation Partnering delivers even greater benefits – cost savings of 50% or more, and where speed is crucial, construction timeframes can be reduced by 80% or more.

- The dramatic improvements in performance delivered by Second and Third Generation Partnering enable construction firms to meet the demands of their customers – whether they need greater certainty, better designs, faster delivery, lower costs, zero defects, guarantees or sophisticated after-care services.

the seven pillars of partnering

A guide to second
generation partnering

The Evolution of the
three Partnering
Generations

chapter 1

The Evolution of the three Partnering Generations

In his seminal report on the UK construction industry Sir Michael Latham firmly advocated the use of Partnering as a way of dramatically improving productivity and profitability. When the Reading Construction Forum published its first report on the subject, *Trusting the Team*, Sir Michael recommended it as an essential introduction to Partnering.

Trusting the Team provides an executive description of Partnering and sets out the business case for using it in all key relationships. Then it tells managers, step by step how to put Partnering into practice on individual projects or on a continuing long-term basis. Finally it provides advice on dealing with the contractual and legal issues raised by Partnering.

The overall message is that Partnering saves money and makes work more enjoyable. It can and should be used widely for construction in the public sector and private sector.

Many clients and firms have subsequently taken Sir Michael's advice to use *Trusting the Team.*

The Construction Industry Board's (CIB) Working Group on Partnering also advocated the same approach in its report *Partnering in the Team* and the European Construction Institute's report *Partnering in the Public Sector* builds on the key messages in *Trusting the Team*.

CIB Working Group 12 describe Partnering as a structured management approach to facilitate teamworking across contractual boundaries. They echo *Trusting the Team* in taking the view that its fundamental components are formalised mutual objectives, agreed problem resolution methods, and an active search for continuous measurable improvements. They emphasise that it should not be confused with other good project management practice, or with long standing relationships, negotiated contracts or preferred supplier arrangements, all of which lack the structure and objective measures that must support a Partnering relationship.

The CIB sees the critical success factor for Partnering as being the commitment of all partners at all levels to make the project a success. The result is that the Partnering agreement, rather than the contract, guides the relationships between parties.

The central message from all this work is that Partnering requires the UK building industry to move away from relying primarily on contractual relationships based on duties and liabilities. This traditional approach generates adversarial attitudes and results in varying performance that on average is significantly lower than that achieved in industries that use Partnering.

How the Construction Industry Board helped firms identify if they really were Partnering in its report *Partnering in the Team*

ARE YOU PARTNERING?

Probably	*Probably not*
You, your boss and senior management right up to the chief executive are convinced that your only sustainable competitive advantage is your ability to enable your people to deliver what they are capable of, and your organisation reflects this belief.	You understand that costs mostly come on two legs. You spend money training those people you aim to keep to do their jobs better. People are kept informed of what is happening in the business on a need-to-know basis.
You selected, or were selected, on the basis of people, quality and price. The selection process was rigorous and all the parties knew what was expected of them.	You submitted the lowest tender. You have not made any profit yet but you are setting up a claim which should put that right.
Through structured workshop sessions you have a clear understanding of what the client wants from the project and what all the other organisations involved in the contract are trying to achieve, including some appreciation of their longer-term strategic goals.	You know that the objective of the exercise is to deliver what is written in the bills of quantities. You understand that everyone else on the job is out to make as much as they can out of it. Other organisation's longer-term strategic goals are not your concern.
Site meetings have a clear agenda. Arguments are robust but positive. Everyone leaves feeling that their point of view has been heard and clear about what they are going to do and by when. You are happy to operate open book accounting and provide free access to all information concerning the contract to the other organisations involved.	Site meetings are run to an agenda set by the project manager. Discussion is carefully worded to avoid any implied acceptance of liability. Issues are often noted, awaiting a formal response, rather than resolved. When things are going wrong, care is taken to establish who is to blame.
You know how much your process costs and its quality characteristics. You know what the best in the industry can do. You know how much better you have to get in the next period and how you are going to do it. You know that if you fail to achive this you will be found out and if you keep failing you'll be thrown out.	You know what the market price for your process is and precisely the minimum standard you should meet.
When things go wrong there is a clear procedure which gets them quickly resolved, by the chief executive if necessary.	When things go wrong you try and sort them out, confirming everything in writing. If it drags on too long or cannot be agreed, claims are made.

Partnering is becoming increasingly well understood in the building industry as a way of working with clients to jointly deliver vastly improved construction performance.

FIRST GENERATION PARTNERING

The early ideas on Partnering revolved around three key principles applied by project teams which research now identifies as:-

● agreeing mutual objectives to take into account the interests of all the firms involved

● making decisions openly and resolving problems in a way that was jointly agreed at the start of a project, and

● aiming at targets that provide continuous measurable improvements in performance from project to project.

This basic approach produces a range of benefits which can be achieved on individual projects (Project Partnering) but are far more significant when applied to a series of projects (Strategic Partnering). The benefits include faster construction times; improved quality; less litigation; improved safety; better teamwork; more innovation and, of course, cost savings of 30%.

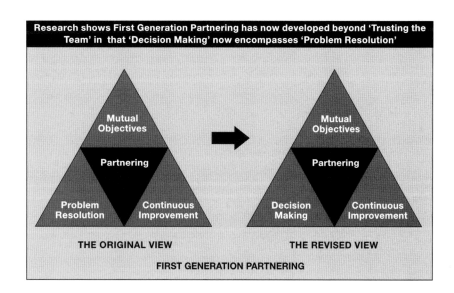

Research shows First Generation Partnering has now developed beyond 'Trusting the Team' in that 'Decision Making' now encompasses 'Problem Resolution'

THE ORIGINAL VIEW · THE REVISED VIEW

FIRST GENERATION PARTNERING

DECIDING WHETHER TO PARTNER

The Construction Industry Board's Working Group 12 take the view that Partnering is not an appropriate procurement strategy for all construction projects or programmes. All forms of Partnering involve risks and costs but the benefits can be very significant indeed, and usually far outweigh any initial investment. When considering Partnering arrangements, parties should seek by discussion to identify sources of risk and then establish who can best assess and manage each of the risks. The Group concluded that Partnering is appropriate where:-

● the project or programme is high value and high risk to the client

● it offers contractors the prospect of a large contribution to their turnover together with secure profits

The research undertaken to support this report shows that the essential first step in Second Generation Partnering is to establish cooperative

relationships – then it is worthwhile looking for better designs and improved technologies. Where organisations concentrate on design and technological innovation without first adopting cooperative relationships, the results often fall short of what could be achieved.

The research demonstrates that Second Generation Partnering is tough and requires sustained commitment from top management to the process of building up the Pillars. Many construction professionals, including some in customer organisations, have a vested interest in maintaining adversarial methods and they have to be won over by clear evidence of the benefits of cooperative behaviour.

Second Generation Partnering is not a panacea and it should be used only where considerable interaction is needed between the firms involved and the work is significant to them.

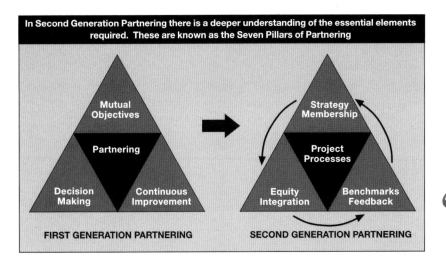

In Second Generation Partnering there is a deeper understanding of the essential elements required. These are known as the Seven Pillars of Partnering

FIRST GENERATION PARTNERING   SECOND GENERATION PARTNERING

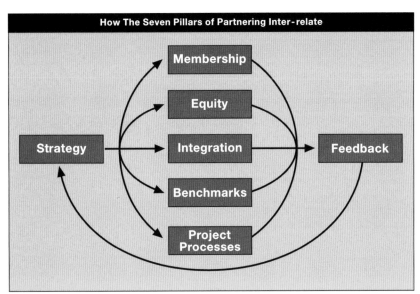

How The Seven Pillars of Partnering Inter-relate

SECOND GENERATION PARTNERING

However, extensive research and analysis now suggests that this approach to Partnering is only the first step, and a new, much more sophisticated 'second generation' style of Partnering has now emerged. This is a genuinely strategic approach that produces significantly greater benefits and can deliver cost savings of up to 40% and can reduce timeframes by 50%, or more.

These developments mean Partnering is now defined in the following terms:

Partnering is a set of strategic actions which embody the mutual objectives of a number of firms achieved by cooperative decision making aimed at using feedback to continuously improve their joint performance.

Second Generation Partnering begins with a strategic decision to cooperate by a client and a group of consultants, contractors and specialists engaged in an ongoing series of projects. Jointly they establish a Strategic Team that builds up 'The Seven Pillars of Partnering.'

The Seven Pillars of Partnering' are:

● Strategy – developing the client's objectives and how consultants, contractors and specialists can meet them on the basis of feedback

● Membership – identifying the firms that need to be involved to ensure all necessary skills are developed and available

● Equity – ensuring everyone is rewarded for their work on the basis of fair prices and fair profits

● Integration – improving the way the firms involved work together by using cooperation and building trust

● Benchmarks – setting measured targets that lead to continuous improvements in performance from project to project

● Project Processes – establishing standards and procedures that embody best practice based on process engineering

● Feedback – capturing lessons from projects and task forces to guide the development of strategy

The Seven Pillars of Partnering' form a controlled system to deal with the rapidly changing markets and technologies that shape today's construction industry. Working together the Pillars provide the basis for individual projects to be carried out efficiently yet enable the Strategic Team to search systematically for ever better designs and ways of working. This combination of efficiency and innovation is the hallmark of leading firms in all modern industries. It is only by breaking free of an over emphasis on projects and developing the habits of strategic thinking and actions that the building industry will make significant improvements to its own performance and reputation in society.

THIRD GENERATION PARTNERING

The research also suggests the emergence of Third Generation Partnering (described in Chapter 6) where the construction industry becomes a modern industry that manufactures and markets products. This vision involves modernised construction firms using Partnering to deal with their regular customers to provide comprehensive packages of products and supporting services. These could include land, new or refurbished facilities, plant and equipment, finance options, and facilities management.

In Third Generation Partnering construction firms work with regular customers to understand their business well enough to see how construction can help it. Occasional and one-off customers are likely to be offered packages, put together on the basis of market research, that give them a choice of standard answers plus a range of options.

In Third Generation Partnering modernised construction firms will use cooperation throughout their supply chains to build up efficient 'virtual

A BLUEPRINT FOR THE FUTURE

Looking at current leading edge practice as three Partnering Generations provides a blueprint for the industry to take control of its own future. It is founded on the three fundamental activities that form the building cycle: use, development and production. Best practice in each of these fundamental areas is essential for really successful projects. Partnering provides a basis for experienced professionals to do their best work. It does this primarily by influencing the interfaces between the fundamental activities so property and construction professionals can work cooperatively with clients and users in producing buildings that people want to invest in.

The following chapters explain in detail the practical changes organisations need to make in their journey towards Third Generation Partnering and provides a step by step guide to Second Generation Partnering.

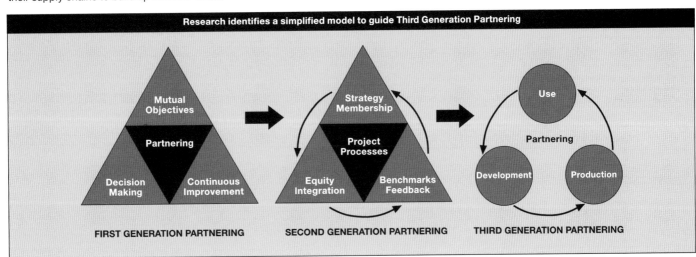

Research identifies a simplified model to guide Third Generation Partnering

FIRST GENERATION PARTNERING   SECOND GENERATION PARTNERING   THIRD GENERATION PARTNERING

organisations' that respond to and shape rapidly changing markets. They will harness new technologies to satisfy customers' expectations. In doing so they will combine the efficiency that comes from standardised processes with the flexibility that comes from creativity and innovation.

Although still in its infancy research suggests cost savings of 50% or more can be achieved by using Third Generation Partnering, and construction timeframes can be reduced by 80% or more if the client's business needs a very fast programme. The dramatic improvements in performance promised by Third Generation Partnering will enable the industry to meet the demands of its customers, whether they need greater certainty, faster delivery, lower costs, zero defects, guarantees or sophisticated after-care services. They also allow construction firms to earn higher levels of profit so they can afford to invest in training and R&D to ensure the future health of their businesses and of our built environment and infrastructure.

The Evolution of the three Partnering Generations

The Effects of the Partnering Generations		
First Generation	**Second Generation**	**Third Generation**
Technology Designers working with contractors to improve designs	Specialists brought into multi-discipline task forces to tackle specific design problems and search for new ideas	Highly industrialised components and modules are manufactured in factories and assembled on site
Processes Design and construction integrated and streamlined	Creative, open decision making guided by well developed management systems	Highly standardised processes are integral to the technology
Clients Involved in project core teams to signal their commitment to partnering	Take strategic decision to partner with industry firms to get better value for money	Marketing of highly developed products and services to broad categories of customers
Teams Adversarial attitudes remain	Training in cooperative behaviour enabling multi-discipline teams to work in open project offices	Integrated teams use supply chain management
Professionals Empowered to use best practice defined by their own professional bodies and education	Empowered to be creative by open decision making in which they are challenged to explain their professional judgements	Multi-discipline professionals competent in design, management and marketing
Basic Workforce Little change except allowed to work more consistently with fewer interruptions	Given the opportunity to put forward ideas for better ways of working	Multi-skilled manufacturers in factories and assemblers on site
Cost Benefits Reduction of up to 30% can be achieved	Reductions of up to 40% can be achieved	Reduction of more than 50% can be achieved
Time Benefits Reductions of up to 40% can be achieved	Reductions of more than 50% can be achieved	Reductions of 80% or more can be achieved
Quality Benefits Quality little changed	Zero defects become a realistic aim	Fully defined and appropriate quality is consistently achieved

the seven pillars of partnering
partnering

A guide to second generation partnering

The Business Case for Second and Third Generation Partnering

Partnering requires commitment, effort and a big investment in time. There are also some 'hard' costs in the form of running workshops, undertaking training and establishing benchmarks. So why bother? What is the real cost, and more importantly, what are the potential returns?

SIMPLE LONG TERM RELATIONSHIPS GENERATE NO BENEFITS!

Many construction businesses already think they are Partnering. They have often worked together for years; there has been lots of repeat business and no major complaints. This 'cosy' approach may provide comfort for the parties involved, but the research on which this report is based suggests there is no evidence to support the view that overall performance is improved, or that simple long term relationships result in faster construction time frames, lower construction costs or better quality work.

THE BENEFITS OF FIRST GENERATION PARTNERING

Analysis of projects that used First Generation Partnering showed that significant benefits were achieved.

Where projects exhibited the hallmarks of simple First Generation Partnering and the team concentrated on cost reduction, savings ranged from 5% to 30%. Where the project teams focused on faster completions, the time savings ranged from 10% to 40%. In the few cases where improving quality was taken seriously, quality levels as measured by snagging lists also improved. Various other performance improvements were also noted – less 'repeat working', less letter writing, and improved safety levels for example.

The research established that these benefits came from people working more effectively. This was shown in the analysis of project team diaries where designers and managers who use Partnering and well developed designs devote 75% of their time to productive work and only 25% to dealing with non-productive matters. For teams whose work is based on simple long-term relationships, or where individual designs are employed, only 40% of managers' time is spent on fruitful management. The clear conclusion of the research was that there is no objective business case for firms operating simple long term relationships; benefits only come as a result of Partnering. This is fundamentally important in planning improvements in performance. There is little point investing in new technology or attempting to improve design unless people learn to work more cooperatively and effectively. Without this culture change they will simply dissipate the planned benefits in non-productive conflict.

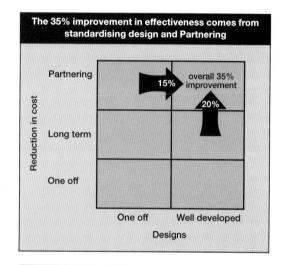

The 35% improvement in effectiveness comes from standardising design and Partnering

THE INCREASED BENEFITS WHEN FIRMS MOVE ON TO SECOND GENERATION PARTNERING

Among those projects that displayed the characteristics of Second Generation Partnering significantly enhanced levels of performance were detected.

Across the sample where cost reduction was the focus, savings of up to 40% were obtained. And where construction timeframes had been the key focus firms delivered savings of 50% or more.

A raft of other benefits are delivered via Second Generation Partnering – including greater certainty, more innovation, improved flexibility, faster starts on site, the elimination of defects at handover, improved value and better design.

Research suggests that the largest benefits are achieved in the design and management stages. The productivity improvements that arise from designers, managers and clients working together for several years range from 50% to 200%.

Clients find that Partnering relationships with contractors are extremely beneficial as they help to reduce the time staff spend going through the same learning curve over and over again. They also encourage continuity of personnel from project to project and so each new project starts at a higher point on the learning curve. The costs associated with bidding are also eliminated for the contractor,

HOW THE RESEARCH INTO THE BENEFITS OF PARTNERING WAS CONDUCTED

Three forms of research were undertaken to look into the impact of Partnering:-

● An analysis was conducted of more than 300 projects. In some 200 of these simple long term relationships existed between contractors, clients and consultants. The aim of this analysis was to see if a simple long term relationship delivered any tangible benefits.

● Teams working on a cross section of construction projects were asked to maintain a detailed 'diary' to identify the percentage of time that was constructively devoted to the management of the project. The different projects included one-off schemes using one-off teams, projects that involved well developed designs and those that involved formal Partnering relationships. The aim of this research was to measure differences in managerial productivity.

● The third element of the research involved the close study of more than 200 specific management actions within well developed Partnering relationships to see how well (or not) the teams succeeded in achieving targets. Did they achieve the cost savings they planned? Did they reduce the timeframe or meet the other performance improvements they had set out to achieve? It was quite straight forward to obtain significant amounts of data on cost and time targets (as these are the targets that project teams actually concentrate on and there are reasonably well-established benchmarks). Where the focus was on other types of improvement – for example improved quality – this was less easy to measure and compare.

and the subsequent savings can be passed on to the client too.

Other benefits include:

● Partnering makes the programming of design and construction work more certain.
● Designers develop an understanding of each others' approach to design and so propose and develop designs in ways that are in tune with each others' ways of thinking.
● Teams are more willing to work together to solve problems.
● The continuity provided by the relationship makes it worth investing in common systems and also provides the flow of profits needed to pay for training and other investment.

Research suggests that Partnering works best when there is somebody - frequently the client - who constantly encourages the project team to set itself tough targets. This gives the team members a real focus and encourages them to continuously improve their work and innovate. When targets are met on one project, they are re-set at a higher level for the next project to ensure that no one becomes complacent. For the targets to be effective, they need to be objectively measured.

Second Generation Partnering changes processes, attitudes and cultures. This is difficult, requires training and consistent leadership from top management.

The successful implementation of a Partnering arrangement will require an initial investment on the part of the organisations involved. Direct costs mainly comprise the cost of workshops, training and the early involvement and commitment of management in establishing the approach. The essential features and the new attitudes are developed at the workshops through the use of a Partnering facilitator. Costs involved at a workshop generally include the hiring of a suitable venue, accommodation and the facilitator's fees. The initial changes in attitude frequently need to be reinforced by training in more efficient methods.

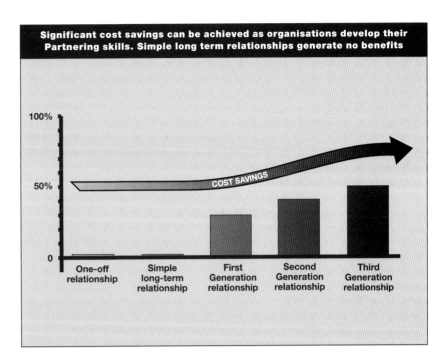

Significant cost savings can be achieved as organisations develop their Partnering skills. Simple long term relationships generate no benefits

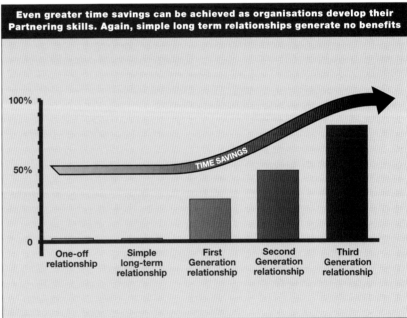

Even greater time savings can be achieved as organisations develop their Partnering skills. Again, simple long term relationships generate no benefits

Case Study - The improvements in speed and costs achieved by Distribution Partnering

In the late 1980's Gazeley Properties developed many large distribution facilities and worked with a limited supply chain of carefully selected consultants, contractors, suppliers and specialists. In 1994 Distribution Partnering was set up to formalise the search for further improvements. As a result each project is set specific targets . Over nine years costs have reduced by almost 40%, construction programmes by more than 40 % and, with Partnering, zero defects have become the consistent aim.

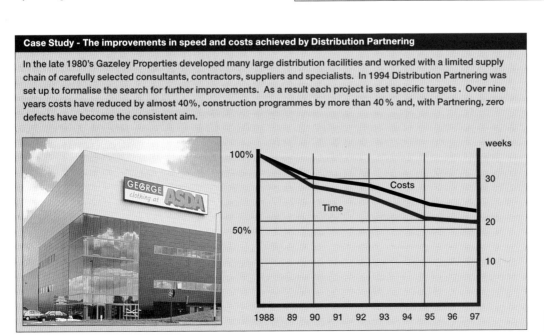

Overall these costs are equivalent to perhaps 1% of the cost of a typical series of construction projects.

The research suggests that the move to Second Generation Partnering provides an excellent return on the investment as savings well in excess of this are consistently delivered.

THE STEP CHANGE IN PERFORMANCE WITH THIRD GENERATION PARTNERING

Analysis of the most progressive partnering organisations suggests that Third Generation Partnering is now beginning to emerge. In this construction firms are taking the initiative to use Partnering in all their relationships to manufacture and market products and supporting services. The research suggests this genuine step change can provide a new level of benefits. The pay-offs appear to be as dramatic as those provided by First Generation Partnering – but after starting from a much higher level of performance in the first place. The data supporting this conclusion is sparse but consistent. The benefits result from the construction industry making fundamental changes to attitudes, organisation and technology – hence the leaps in performance shown in the diagram opposite.

Research among the relatively small handful of projects that currently exhibit the characteristics of Third Generation Partnering suggest that cost savings of 50% can be achieved and, where the reduction of time is the key focus, this can be cut by 80% or more. These massive improvements in efficiency enable the industry to concentrate on adding value for its customers and earn sensible profit levels.

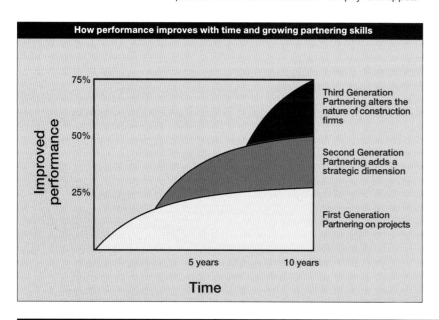

How performance improves with time and growing partnering skills

Improved performance / Time

Third Generation Partnering alters the nature of construction firms

Second Generation Partnering adds a strategic dimension

First Generation Partnering on projects

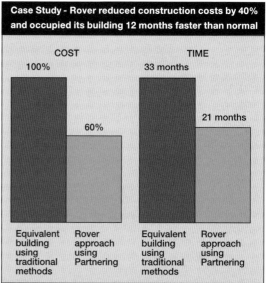

Case Study - Rover reduced construction costs by 40% and occupied its building 12 months faster than normal

COST — 100%, 60%
TIME — 33 months, 21 months

Equivalent building using traditional methods / Rover approach using Partnering

Case Study - Sainsbury's has reduced construction costs by almost 40% and more than halved construction timeframes over the last six years

In the early 1990's Sainsbury's achieved significant cost and time savings by moving over to Construction Management, and through reducing its supplier base. Its move to Second Generation Partnering began in 1994. The current partnering strategy provides well developed standards and procedures that allow its mainstream supermarkets to be produced quickly and efficiently. They also provide the basis for continuous improvements in performance.

In 1994 the Sainsbury's team had been focusing on building its supermarkets faster and faster. Its Banbury project - completed at the end of the year - was constructed in a record 24 weeks by RGCM. Sainsbury's challenged RGCM to build the next stores in 18 weeks using the same partnering principles.

The next mainstream store was completed for £9.6 million – £200,000 under budget and 10% below previous costs. Quality was not compromised and a high standard of workmanship was delivered - indeed the goal of zero defects was almost achieved. The project was completed in just 17 weeks (the norm for this size of store was 32 to 34 weeks).

A month before this project was completed Sainsbury's rewarded the team with the news that it would be commissioned for two new stores.

Both projects went well and were completed between 5 and 10% below Sainsbury's very tough construction cost model, Progress was also made towards the goal of zero defects and one scheme was completed a week and a half ahead of target; the other was finished in a record 15 weeks.

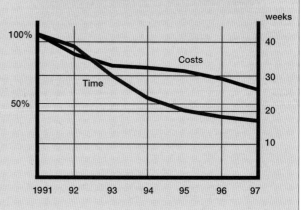

Costs / Time

1991 92 93 94 95 96 97

weeks: 40, 30, 20, 10

the seven pillars of partnering

A guide to second generation partnering

Partnering

Journeys

3

chapter

How to 'read' the Case Study Journeys

The research into the case studies showed there was no single 'route' to Second and Third Generation Partnering. All the teams started from different points, and followed different routes – but they've all essentially been aiming at the same journey's end. On the way they've each assembled their seven pillars of partnering, but often in a different order.

To illustrate the case study journeys a graphical representation has been developed that endeavours to reinforce this. On our illustrative 'map', you'll find a detailed explanation of how Second and sometimes Third Generation Partnering developed. By the time the team reaches the end of each of these journeys it will have assembled the seven pillars of partnering. At each step in the journey the new Pillars which have been added are identified.

In the journey to Second and Third Generation Partnering certain learning points have been highlighted.

At the end of the journey the team can use the Pillars to metaphorically cross the Rubicon.

The second illustration revolves around a 'Temple' and highlights one example from each partnering organisation's work where all seven pillars are in place. In most cases these describe individual projects but the BAA and Esso cases are each supported by descriptions of self-contained strategic arrangements.

By studying the strategic journeys and the specific case study examples other firms in the construction industry should be able to identify where they currently are and what else needs to be tackled in order for them to use Second Generation Partnering to get them to the point where they can 'cross the Rubicon' to begin Third Generation Partnering.

Key

| Strategy | Membership | Equity | Integration | Benchmarks | Project Processes | Feedback |

The graphic 'icons' shown above have been used to indicate which Pillars have been put in place at each stage in the journey. Boxes shown in blue follow the main 'route'. Those in maroon indicate various learning points that emerged along the journey

the seven pillars of partnering

A guide to second generation partnering

How Whitbread's Partnering strategy developed

International competition forced Whitbread to set a tough target for reducing construction costs. In the past the company had organised construction through its separate businesses on a one-off project basis. It was recognised that little improvement in performance would be possible unless this approach was changed.

This led Whitbread's construction directors to look for similarities in their work rather than concentrating on differences. Recognising the similarities gave them the basis to use Strategic Partnering with consultants, contractors and key suppliers.

The Second Generation pillars are now largely in place and are delivering significant improvements in performance. The project case study shows how cost savings equivalent to 19% were achieved.

See overleaf for the journey...

How Whitbread's Road to Partnering Developed

THE BACKGROUND

Whitbread builds around 100 new projects a year collectively worth approximately £300 million. Each of Whitbread's business units (Beefeater, Inns, Marriott and Travel Inn) used to procure new construction work by individually tendering each project. This may have produced competitive prices, but it didn't always result in good quality or speed and did not encourage innovation.

THE COST OF ONE-OFF TENDERING

One-off tendering resulted in more and more builders working for the company, each one having to climb the same learning curve. This approach focused on contractors doing everything possible to maintain their margins, rather than searching for new solutions. It also tended to foster adversarial attitudes and claims.

1994: THE IMPACT OF THE LATHAM REPORT

Whitbread was impressed by the Latham Report. The company agreed that the UK construction industry lagged behind many other countries. Whitbread accepted that the way forward was to reduce the adversarial practices and move over to Partnering. The company also agreed that this initiative would have to be led by the construction industry's clients.

1995: WHITBREAD INVESTIGATES A NEW APPROACH

Whitbread commissioned John Allen, a former Chairman of John Laing Management Limited, to prepare a report on how it could develop its approach to Partnering. This concluded that because the different businesses used different standard approaches to tender each project, it was inefficient, and that substantial savings could be obtained by working in partnership with a limited number of contractors. The new initiative was spearheaded by a Partnership Working Group that reported to Whitbread's Property Procurement Committee.

THE PARTNERSHIP WORKING GROUP

The Partnership Working Group was set up to develop Whitbread's strategy for partnering on new construction. The Group included representation from all businesses involved in new construction – Beefeater, Inns, Hotels and TGI Fridays. The Group had two main objectives:-

- Maximise the cross-divisional benefit
- Evaluate the costs and benefits of the new approach and implement a way of achieving and recording continuous improvement

IDENTIFYING POTENTIAL PARTNERS

Each property department was asked to nominate potential contractors. Forty six were initially proposed and each asked to complete a detailed questionnaire. These were then analysed, and the list was reduced to 26. Each firm was then asked to price the management of a typical project and present at interview details of its experience and policies for Quality Control, Health & Safety, IT, Partnering, etc. From this process 16 companies were felt to have a compatible culture and the financial and management strength Whitbread wanted.

These 16 firms were then asked to price typical projects for Beefeater, Brewers Fayre, Travel Inn and TGI Fridays. These submissions were examined carefully in the following areas:-

- Profit and overhead structure
- Their on site subcontractors management skills
- Prices paid for subcontract packages
- Suggestions for potential improvements to the product and process
- Their understanding of Whitbread's specific requirements and methods
- Their understanding of Partnering

After further analysis the list was whittled down to six firms, all of whom were visited by senior representatives and Directors of all Whitbread's businesses to confirm cultural and business fit between the companies.

THE SEARCH FOR SIMILARITIES

In the past Whitbread had perceived all the buildings produced for its various divisions as very different. However, when it really examined the cross section of projects it commissioned it discovered that most cost about £1m, took 20-22 weeks on site, were one or two storey and had similar sized floor areas.

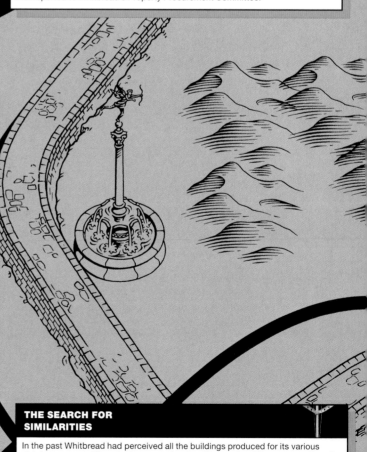

THE MISSION

The project team assembled to build the restaurant and Travel Inn had a good understanding of Whitbread's requirements due to its ongoing partnering relationship. This had been helped by the standardisation of the product and the process. The project team's mission was to produce the very best value for money within an improving time frame without sacrificing quality. The Swindon project was viewed as part of the learning curve within a Strategic Partnering arrangement.

SORTING OUT THE MONEY

Money is dealt with strategically in a way that reduces the possibility of adversarial attitudes and cost cutting.

INTEGRATED TECHNOLOGIES

Whitbread commonly builds a Beefeater Restaurant and a Travel Inn together under one contract. The company uses different technologies for the two buildings – timber frame and steel frame. Both are sensible choices for the buildings considered in isolation, but together they can complicate the construction process when key trades do not coincide. The buildings often become weather tight at different times, and plant and equipment is needed at different times. Pearce, the main contractor for the project, put together a task force that was given three weeks to devise a design that provided a simpler process. The task force included the operators, design consultants, specialist contractors and Pearce's own design and construction staff. By understanding the needs of the interior spaces better they were able to design a timber frame solution for both buildings which simplified the process.

LESSONS FOR THE FUTURE

The Swindon project was significant in that:-

- It provided an opportunity to re-evaluate sub-contract works and develop downstream Partnering with specialist contractors.

- The timber frame package was rationalised by excluding doors, windows, floating floor and drylining (all of which had previously been included). Economies were achieved by dealing directly with specialists in each of these activities.

- This produced some grey areas between the packages, but valuable lessons were learnt and a basis established for processes on future projects to be refined.

INNOVATIONS

Value Engineering identified ideas for improvements, including:

- Substitution of felt with a breather membrane for expensive dry ridge and eave vents; (£7,000 savings)

- Single membrane flat roof in lieu of upside down ballasted asphalt roof (£4,000 savings)

- Rationalisation of foundation layout to save time and money

- Revision of car park levels to avoid excess cartaway

- UPVC featured prominently in external finishings, eg Travel Inn windows, fascia, soffit and shiplap.

- Maintenance costs were reduced by the use of a self colour render which eliminated the need for re-decoration.

- All these (and other) ideas were received in a proactive way with none of the usual suspicions of 'hidden agendas' that come with the conventional process.

COST CONTROL

Whitbread takes its budget very seriously. For example, when the planners wanted clay tiles rather than the concrete tiles this was going to add £20,000 to the costs. Pearce looked for savings and found that by using a breather felt instead of vents this saved £7,000. The rest of the cost was found from a variety of other small savings and by using some of the agreed contingency allowance.

USING STANDARDS TO REDUCE COSTS

The simplified process that was developed has now become Whitbread's new standard. Within the first year of using it, construction costs have been reduced by 20% and construction time by one week. There are now plans to make a further reduction in construction time of seven weeks – effectively a total reduction of 34%.

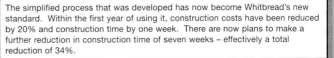

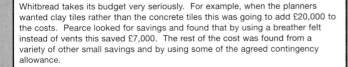

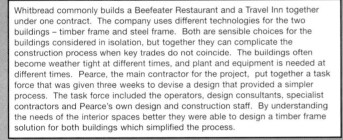

PARTNE

STRATEGY

MEMBERSHIP

EQUITY

INTEGRATION

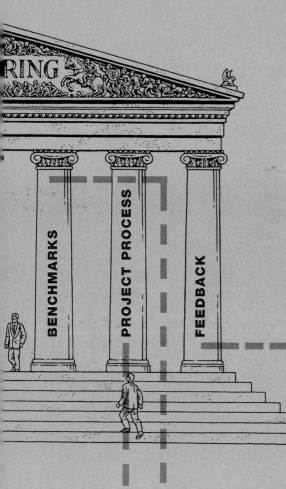

RING

BENCHMARKS

PROJECT PROCESS

FEEDBACK

£335,000 was saved on this Beefeater and Travel Inn

THE FEEDBACK LOOP

The construction team had already worked through a complete partnership project on a very similar scheme in Bristol. The team's involvement in the second scheme meant many lessons were passed on, and new lessons were learnt for the future. All members of the construction team worked hard to understand the precise building required and they were all pro-active in improving processes to complete the final product efficiently. The lessons from both the Bristol and Swindon projects are now considered almost second nature by the project team.

WORKING TOGETHER

The number of letters produced during the Swindon project decreased by more than 40%. The atmosphere between team members gradually relaxed as the project proceeded. All parties understood they were working to the same ends. Bad weather during the sub-structure and early brickwork phase and unexpected piling works could have given reasons to claim for an extension of time. The partnering approach brought a whole hearted commitment from the project team to complete within the time constraints identified and to absorb and work around problems, rather than to capitalise on them to gain profit and time advantage. The extra £8,000 cost of piling and ground beams was absorbed within the original build cost and the project was considered by most to be both a refreshing and enjoyable construction experience. The construction team has now worked through a complete partnership project. The change in philosophy has been dramatic – from the attitude of the site foreman to the quantity surveyors working on the settlement of final accounts. Across the whole team there has been a distinct effort to understand the final product required by Whitbread. Improved processes, clearer understanding of Whitbread's operational requirements and value engineering achievements will all be taken on to the next project and fed back into future design and procurement. The team's skill in dealing with Whitbread's operational requirements immediately before and after handover improved. The co-ordination of direct suppliers and sub-contractors also improved significantly. The team is now familiar with Whitbread's key programme requirements, the optimum sequence of events and key milestones.

PROJECT OBJECTIVES AND ACHIEVEMENTS

The achievements can be measured by comparing the Swindon scheme with a similar project at Emersons Green, Bristol carried out six months earlier. Taking account of differences in size and the faster completion of the Swindon project, the total benefit to Whitbread was £335,000 - or almost 19% of the capital cost. In addition there were improvements in customer satisfaction and service quality. The building is regarded as good in terms of aesthetic design quality.

the seven pillars of partnering

A guide to second
generation partnering

How Sainsbury's Partnering strategy developed

Sainsbury's builds about 25 new supermarkets a year using Strategic Partnering. The strategic dimension is largely implicit. The journey illustrates that on Sainsbury's projects for it's mainstream superstores best practice is already well established and that the company has now assembled all its Second Generation project pillars. The case study describes the Ecostore where the project core team was set targets that required large improvements in performance that have now been achieved from partnering.

See overleaf for the journey...

How Sainsbury's Road to Partnering Developed

SAINSBURY'S ADOPTS CONSTRUCTION MANAGEMENT

In the 1980's Sainsbury's efforts to improve cost and time were frustrated by traditional contractors forming barriers around the specialist contractors. To overcome this in 1989 Sainsbury's undertook its first project using a Construction Management contract. This created a set of relationships that had many of the features we now call partnering. Construction Management helped Sainsbury's take the 'easy fat out of the process' by working on the policy of 'if you can't see it, don't spend money on it!'. The team shifted towards focusing more on the end product and began to limit the designers' freedom by defining standards. Construction Management produced significant improvements in performance but it became increasingly difficult to find further improvements.

THE INTRODUCTION OF PERFORMANCE SPECIFICATIONS

In 1994, Sainsbury's introduced performance specifications. Previously, Sainsbury's had standards for most of the items within its buildings, but it now shifted firmly away from these and towards using British Standard products which could be bought off the shelf. This caused less hassle for the consultants and reduced costs for the client as it did not have to maintain its own standards.

THE BIG SQUEEZE & THE MOVE TO OUTSOURCING

In April 1994 Sainsbury's became involved an intense price war with other supermarkets. The financial return was too low and the Main Board wanted the costs of stores to be reduced significantly. Sainsbury's went through a down-sizing process that it called Genesis. The Property Division reduced from 240 to 80 staff and its northern office was shut, leaving just the east and west. The Division reduced its project managers from 20 to 12. In parallel to this Sainsbury's hit a new problem when the Department of the Environment virtually stopped giving planning permission for out of town stores. Sainsbury's strategy for maintaining its share price had been to increase the size of the sales area each year, but it had no existing planning approvals and no land bank. The decision was therefore made to extend the size of existing stores. This effectively involved more work per sq ft than when it built new stores, and Sainsbury's Property Division now had fewer staff to do it. These factors forced Sainsbury's to outsource more of its work, which in turn meant it needed to work more closely with its suppliers.

REDUCTION OF SUPPLY BASE

Due to these pressures, Sainsbury's decided to reduce its supplier base so it could use Partnering with carefully selected companies. The company accepted that it would require new project management skills. It also recognised that if it were to partner more its suppliers would get a greater continuity of work. In selecting partners, Sainsbury's concentrated on its long standing suppliers as it knew their strengths and weaknesses. Mutual trust had also developed with these suppliers and cooperative ways of working had already been established. The process of reducing its supplier base resulted in the number of architects it used being reduced from 36 to six firms and its list of contractors fell from 32 to just three. The need for new management skills, however, resulted in the introduction of four new construction management firms to provide tough cost and time control systems.

INTERNAL PARTNERING

In line with reducing its supplier base, Sainsbury's realised it had to change the attitudes of its own staff by adopting internal partnering. This was achieved by instilling the Total Quality Management culture. Staff were encouraged to be more flexible and out-going. This new culture was not formalised in procedures, but was implicit in the new way of working. This strategy began to reveal individuals' strengths and weaknesses and identified challenges for improvement. The internal team also began to recognise why it needed to map its processes in order to find improvements in performance.

EARLY PARTNERING

Following all the changes Sainsbury's had less backup internally for its project managers so it needed to be able to trust and partner more with outside contractors. A strategy document was presented to the Main Board based on one project where it had saved £100,000 by getting the project team to cooperate in a joint search for savings. The document recommended that Sainsbury's changed the way it procured its buildings and Partnering was put forward as the answer for the future. The Property Division's performance on construction projects at that time was variable, but improving. Sainsbury's developed a model project designed to make a 30% reduction in cost. Of the previous ten stores it had built the target costs for individual elements were achieved on about half the projects but only two projects were within overall model costs. The model produced a construction period of 28 weeks. Only two of the previous ten stores had achieved this, so Sainsbury's felt it needed to look for a new way of reliably delivering faster construction timeframes.

THE TQM VISION AT SAINSBURY'S

Within Sainsbury's TQM means empowering people to represent the company and to take new initiatives.

The pursuit of better standards, more effective methods of working, a more innovative approach to tasks, and a greater responsibility for taking initiatives are now becoming part of normal work in the Property Division.

A change in attitude and culture has occurred across the Division.

Sainsbury's Ecostore

DEVELOPING THE MISSION

Schal was approached as Construction Management Partners in September 1996 and invited to attend a workshop with other design consultants to discuss ideas for reducing the construction costs of a new concept store – the Ecostore – that was to be designed from scratch with a clean brief. Schal was selected because it knew Sainsbury's business well, was committed to Partnering and had proven value engineering skills. Sainsbury's was concerned about taking a big risk with its image as it was targeting to cut the construction costs dramatically. Therefore a lot of careful up-front thinking and planning was required. Various ideas were floated at the workshop and Schal undertook to develop and cost these ideas for a follow up workshop. At this point a number of specialist contractors were involved in the process to aid the development of new ideas.

ACCEPTANCE OF A NEW CONCEPT STORE

At the follow up workshop the principle of the new Ecostore was accepted and the team was given the task of developing the ideas for presentation to the Sainsbury's Board. Throughout the autumn of 1996 the new concept evolved and was then drawn up and priced. The outline concept was presented to the Board and consequently received approval. The team was then tasked with developing it further with a view to getting approval to build a trial store at Leigh. Part of this process involved the setting up of task forces to look at all aspects of the new concept.

DEVELOPING THE NEW STORE

Schal was represented at all the task force meetings and asked to bring together all the findings. During this period many innovations were explored, each resulting in dramatic cost savings. These included the use of a new steel frame, a new floor system to replace the traditional terrazzo tiles, a different cladding system and an entirely new interior. The design was put to Sainsbury's Main Board and the overall concept and budget was approved.

A TRIAL PROJECT

In January 1997 full Board approval was granted for the trial store to be constructed in Leigh. The team then began to further develop the design to fit the site. Early designs were judged too radical and so the budget was increased to ensure that the quality would match Sainsbury's image. In February three proposals were presented to the Board, which were scored in terms of cost, appearance, practicality and buildability. One of these was accepted and a new cost target was agreed. This represented just more than a 30% reduction in costs compared with Sainsbury's latest normal superstore. After further research and development, including constructing mock up displays, lighting and checkouts, the scheme was fully endorsed, and work commenced on site in June 1997.

PARTNERING WORKSHOP

A two-day workshop was set up for the project just before commencement on site. This enabled the design team and contractors to meet, discuss and understand the concept of Partnering within the Sainsbury's framework. The workshop also helped to engender a spirit of openness and trust. At the end of the workshop relationships had already bonded. The construction phase ran fairly smoothly as all the planning and development had been carried out up-front.

THE PARTNERING CHARTER

At the workshop the team completed a Partnering Charter. An excerpt follows:

We, as a team are committed within a partnering framework to deliver a quality, new concept supermarket to meet the expectations of all our customers.

We will achieve this goal through teamwork within a trusting and open environment borne out of communication, cooperation and coordination.

Our objectives:

- *Improve and further relationships*
- *Success of concept*
- *Profitability for all concerned*
- *Complete on time, within budget and safely*
- *Defects free*
- *Right first time*
- *Establish project/partnering benchmark*
- *Continuous Improvement*

STEELFRAME

A modular repetitive grid design was produced for maximum efficiency. This was achieved by developing the most economical possible steelframe and then designing the rest of the building around it. Loads on the frame were reduced by locating the services equipment and plant at the back of the building, not on the roof.

The whole building layout was so repetitive that one basic detail for the steelframe was sufficient to provide all the production drawings.

A saving of 29% was achieved compared to Sainsbury's usual frames.

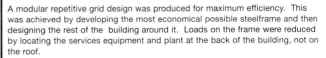

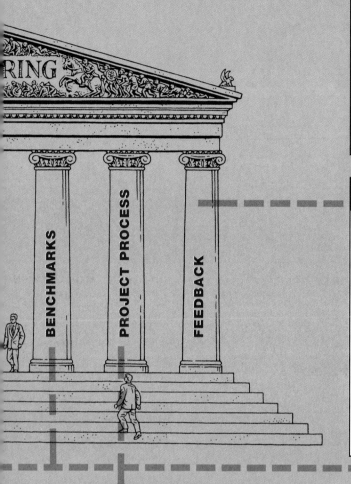

RING

BENCHMARKS

PROJECT PROCESS

FEEDBACK

Sainsbury's Ecostore was built for 32% less

IMPROVEMENTS ACHIEVED

The following table illustrates the percentage improvement achieved on the Leigh project compared to a standard model:

	-60%	-40%	-20%	0	+20%
Foundations					
Lowest Floor – Topmix Topaz					
Structural Frame					
Non Loadbearing Envelope					
Lobby/Canopy					
Internal Divisions					
Plumbing Services					
Internal Finishes – Matrix Design					
Fittings & Equipment					
Specified Supplier Fittings					
BWIC with M&E Services					
Refrigeration					
Electrical Installation					
Environmental Installation					
Mechanical Handling					
Standby Generator					
TOTAL					

CONSTRUCTION INNOVATIONS

Task forces were set up to tackle specific issues. One of these was responsible for developing a new and more economic flooring system.

Terrazzo tiles are used in traditional Sainsbury's supermarkets and are a big cost item. Topmix was approached by the Ecostore team to produce a new type of finished concrete floor.

An initial trial could not achieve the colour balance and quality that Sainsbury's wanted. Sainsbury's kept faith in Topmix to satisfactorily develop the new floor system. Topmix tried a new approach involving a new material that was both stronger and could be ground and polished. Because it was strong the new floor was half as thick as traditional floors. Initially this solution was too slippery when wet, so a lower level of polish was applied with a sealer, to achieve a semi-matt surface.

Other elements had to be redesigned to take full advantage of the new material -for example all services are in the roof to eliminate the need for floor ducts.

The resulting product, Topaz, greatly reduced costs and programme. Many samples of floor were laid for inspection and feedback. The final solution only emerged after several months of hard work and development. This flooring system has massive potential in buildings requiring a hard wearing finish and is already being considered for use on other projects.

The same floor has been used throughout the store, right into the store rooms. On the Ecostore project the new floor produced a 40% cost saving, and will also result in long-term maintenance cost reductions.

RESULTS

The building looks aesthetically good, though different from a traditional Sainsbury's store. With construction time down to 16 weeks and cost savings equivalent to 32%, new landmarks were achieved without compromising safety and quality. Other benefits include a reduction in long-term maintenance costs and the potential for future work for all members of the project team.

CLADDING

ne of the specific project objectives was to design a new glazing system which as to be visually better than before and produce a cost saving.

he cladding was developed by a task force that included the glazing ontractors, The Window Glass Company. The Task Force was appointed early nd so had time to explore several options. The solution was based on evelopments originally undertaken for the Esso service station shop fronts, but a much larger scale.

he result is visually exciting, brings more light into the store and produced avings of 29%.

INTERIORS

The interiors inside the Ecostore are all new and produced a dramatic 32% cost saving. Examples of how the savings were achieved include:

- The ceiling was taken out, exposing the services

- The M&E systems were totally re-thought. Traditional Sainsbury's stores have the same temperature throughout, but the Ecostore is heated from zone to zone depending on the planned use.

- The staff offices were re-designed to a different configuration, producing smaller areas with open plan spaces. As a result the store is operated differently and the running costs are lower. This has also reduced the insurance costs for the building.

the seven pillars of partnering

A guide to second generation partnering

How Distribution Partnering's strategy developed

Distribution Partnering has the following members:

Gazeley Properties (developers)

Chetwood Associates (architects)

Edward Roscoe Associates (structural engineers)

Kelly Taylor & Associates (service engineers)

Simons Group (contractors)

W H Stephens & Sons (quantity surveyors)

The University of Reading (research)

Gazeley Properties is the UK's leading distribution facilities developer. The company had for some time used informal long-term relationships with consultants, contractors and key suppliers to achieve continuous improvements in performance from project to project.

By trial and error it had adopted many features of Partnering. To ensure continued improvements Gazeley, with its leading consultants and contractors, undertook a performance review to identify challenges that still needed attention. The review identified Strategic Partnering as a powerful tool to generate further improvements.

Distribution Partnering was set up by Gazeley and its main consultants and contractors to put Strategic Partnering into effect and the new organisation is already delivering significant improvements over its already excellent performance. The specific project analysed in the case study journey was a new Asda clothing warehouse in Northamptonshire. The team delivered this huge building in just 22 weeks, with minimal defects and at a cost of just £22 per sq ft.

See overleaf for the journey...

How Distribution Partnering's Road to Partnering Developed

THE BACKGROUND

Gazeley Properties had worked with a consistent team of consultants, contractors and key specialist contractors for more than ten years. These relationships were successful and, working together, the team produced outstanding results in terms of costs and times.

EARLY EXPLORATIONS INTO THE WORLD OF PARTNERING

The team began to have early discussions about entering into a formal Partnering arrangement in the middle of 1994. In order to make Partnering work, the team felt the following issues needed to be addressed:

n   Clarify the benefits of Partnering

n   How would the extra costs from setting up the Partnership be paid for?

n   What would happen when the Partnership created new relationships - for example if the architects were required to do less and the engineers do more?

n   How could the partnership ensure that the allocation of fees was fair?

n   Fees needed to be discussed openly, so that everyone knew who was doing what and what they were being paid for their work.

n   How would new investments for the benefit of the whole team be paid for?

n   How could Partnering ensure reasonable continuity of work for each firm?

TEN POTENTIAL CHALLENGES

The team began its work by asking each member to produce a list of the ten major challenges that impeded the efficient running of projects. The team then identified ideas for overcoming these hurdles.

KEY INITIATIVES

The principle ideas that emerged were:

n   Base the Brief for each new project on a previous design that worked well

n   Bring everyone in at the start, including the subcontractors

n   Form fair and clear contracts

n   Decide who is responsible for which aspects of design approval

n   Get a clear plan of fixed achievable milestones that cover every aspect of the work, including all communication and information flows

n   Set a timed agenda of predetermined topics at all standard meetings

n   Hold team building exercises for the project teams

FIVE YEAR PLAN

The team then established a Strategic Team and called itself 'Distribution Partnering'. It then set itself objectives for five years so that by the year 2000 its performance would be unmatched in Europe. It was recognised that achieving this aim required radical changes to the development, design, technology, construction and aftercare services of large distribution facilities. The team aim to make the activity a customer service. Over the five years Distribution Partnering wants to make the quality of its products and services absolutely reliable. This means that the norm will be zero defects at handover and all the promised services will be provided totally reliably. Where a failure occurs, it will be put right without question and without cost to the tenant or owner. Distribution Partnering's target is to complete exactly on time – to the day – by setting and meeting key milestones leading to the agreed handover date. Over five years the team has set itself the goal of designing and constructing a large distribution facility in just three months (excluding delays caused by planning and other regulatory bodies). Distribution Partnering also wants to reduce the capital costs of large distribution facilities by at least 30% in real terms; and make similar improvements in total life cycle costs. The agreed Five Year Plan also identified a desire to widen the team's service to finding land and finance, providing technical advice on the use of large distribution facilities, and providing fitting out, commissioning, maintaining and facilities management services.

STRATEGIC INITIATIVES

Many strategic initiatives have been undertaken to achieve the tough goals set in Distribution Partnering's Five Year Plan. These include

n   Benchmarking current performance against the best in the world

n   Producing a quality assurance document to describe Distribution Partnering

n   Setting up task forces of specialist contractors and consultants for each major construction element

n   Setting up a database of well established standard details to provide a focus for feedback, avoiding defects and improvements

n   Establishing attitudes and procedures that deliver zero defects

n   Developing effective control over project programmes

n   Developing effective cost control procedures so the team can meet ever tougher cost targets without reducing quality or risking late completions

n   Integrating the partners' CAD systems to create a virtual design office

n   Exploring the use of large scale manufactured components and prefabricated elements to achieve substantial reductions in construction times

n   Developing an attractive aftercare package and marketing it as the best available for tenants and owners of large distribution facilities

n   Making themselves the automatic choice for quality service and cost effectiveness.

New Warehouse for Asda at Brackmills

INTRODUCTION

Lessons learned from both the Hemel Hempstead and the Asda SAC projects were taken on board for Distribution Partnering's project for Gazeley at Brackmills in Northampton. This scheme involved building a 2,800m² clothing warehouse for Asda. Distribution Partnering agreed to provide the required facility for an agreed fixed price. At this stage there was no precise design or programme. Gazeley turned to Distribution Partnering as a tried and tested team that it believed would deliver. Underlying this bold approach was an acceptance that each member would get a fair return for their work. For example, as the extent of the design work needed became clear, consultants' fees were adjusted to ensure that the expectation of a fair return became a reality.

A TOUGH SET OF TARGETS

Distribution Partnering's agreement with Asda was bold. For example, the lead-in time before starting on site was just one week and the construction period was only 22 weeks. This was achieved by using an existing design and the standard architectural design details developed by the architects, Chetwood Associates, so that a set of indicative drawings was available on Day One. A firm price of £22 per sq ft was quickly established because the quantity surveyors had extensive data based on similar schemes. This figure effectively meant that costs had been held constant for more than two years. The team adopted Distribution Partnering's policy of aiming for zero defects using ideas developed at Hemel and Asda SAC.

CORE TEAM

All the firms were represented in the core team by experienced professionals hand picked for the project. An important advantage was that many had already worked together on Asda SAC, including the developer's project manager and the client's representative. A deliberate policy was to get everyone involved in the project to trust other people and to continue to do so as long as they acted in ways that justified the trust. This was a demonstration of good faith and Partnering in action. The team was motivated by an implicit assurance of future work as long as the project went well. Simons, the design build contractor, was appointed on the basis of negotiation, initially as a management contractor. Once the design and price were sufficiently developed to identify and quantify the risks, the contract was changed to a design and build basis. Simons' team was hand picked and was highly motivated to achieve a successful project.

DESIGN

The main warehouse structure used an existing scheme design because if offered flexibility. This solution was not altered. It employed known technologies and details were produced jointly by the core team and the specialist contractors. The fast start on site made it inevitable that design overlapped with construction. With this in mind the management of the design was carefully re-thought. A Design Manager was appointed to ensure that specialist contractors had all the information they needed to complete the detailed design on time and that further information arrived in time for construction to be carried out in accordance with the programme.

MANAGING MEETINGS

Workshops were used early in the project to review decision making and agree an effective pattern and style of meetings. All the firms working on site included a person with the authority to commit their firm to action. Challenges were therefore resolved quickly, mainly because the right people attended (including the client). The distribution of information was carefully thought out to ensure that people got only the information they needed to enable them to do their jobs properly.

TIME CONTROL

Time was given the highest priority. The planning and control of the programme were appropriately thorough and involved everyone. The programme tried to identify risks early and agree how each risk should be handled. Weekly programmes were produced in agreement with the specialist contractors and there were daily meetings to resolve challenges and plan the next day's work. The overall effect was that progress was very carefully monitored and any problems were quickly identified and dealt with.

COST CONTROL

Cost was taken seriously, but was controlled in a manner that recognised the primary importance of time. A detailed cost plan based on a firm scheme design and expressed in work packages was agreed early by all the key parties. The overall budget included a sensible contingency. An important benefit of Partnering was that the consultant quantity surveyor and the contractor's quantity surveyor formed an integrated commercial management team. Whichever of them was best able to undertake each cost control task did it, and they shared the results. They maintained their individual responsibilities but produced just one record of the project costs, avoiding any duplication of effort.

PARTNE

STRATEGY

MEMBERSHIP

EQUITY

INTEGRATION

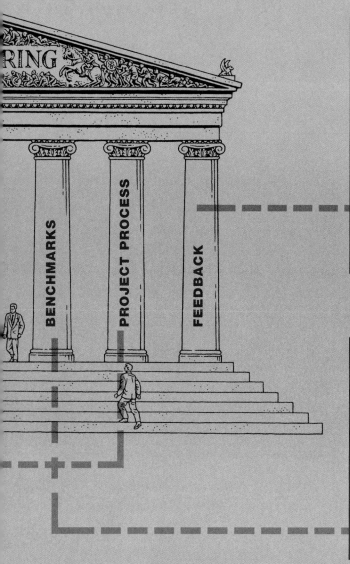

FEEDBACK INTO THE STRATEGIC DIMENSION

A two day workshop was held at the end of the project to collect feedback from the specialist contractors. Useful lessons for future Distribution Partnering projects included:

- Decide on the Brief as early as possible
- Try to ensure that the customer understands construction, as this helps the team deliver
- Set specific objectives for the project
- Match the project team to the specific needs of the project
- Where speed is vital use an established core team
- Investigate and evaluate risks
- Use known technologies or make explicit provision for innovation
- Use tough cost, time and quality control systems
- Agree a problem resolution process
- Ensure that all meetings have clearly defined purposes
- Ensure that lessons are fed into future projects.

PROJECT OUTCOMES

The project was a success because:

- The team had worked together before, so everyone trusted each other
- All the key people were willing to get the job done whatever it took
- Clear objectives had been established at the outset
- The project had a good client who understood construction
- Very positive attitudes throughout the team
- Daily on site planning and problem solving
- A no blame culture was achieved

The project was completed within the budget initially agreed. The team also managed to include a number of valuable features that went beyond what was originally promised. The construction costs are the lowest that Distribution Partnering has achieved and the quality is well above average. Construction work was also significantly faster than previous Distribution Partnering norms.

THE SPECIALIST CONTRACTORS

The specialist contractors were carefully selected by the core team. Most had already carried out several projects for Distribution Partnering. This helped encourage open teamworking. On occasions specialist contractors put extra resources into the project to maintain the programme. They also helped each other, even though this cost them management time and extra money. At the Final Workshop all specialist contractors confirmed that the project was a success from their point of view.

EXPLORING COMMUNICATIONS TECHNOLOGY & PREFABRICATION

Progress was made towards using an IT based intranet to connect the site to where consultants and specialist contractors were working on the project. This speeded up design development – for example it was not uncommon for a change to be identified on site one day and the consultants and specialists to have agreed new details and priced them in agreement with the factory manager ready for a decision the next. The approach was severely tested when the team designed the offices. The very short lead in time meant that once discussions with the users had taken place there was no time left to use traditional construction methods. As a result the prefabricated option was revisited and adopted as the best option. This allowed the project to be completed on time. However, the team's over hurried approach meant the offices were not as successful as the team had hoped. This area was not as fully finished as the team had expected, it was installed late, and there were quality control problems.

QUALITY CONTROL

Quality control was taken very seriously. Known quality problems were designed out largely by using standard drawings. The specialists accepted responsibility for the quality of their own work. An important factor in this is that the data supporting the standard drawings was used to encourage them to focus on known problem areas. They produced snagging lists monthly and on completion of their work. In addition quality was checked by the core team members at every site visit. The various snagging lists were discussed at Progress Meetings with the specialists. The final snagging list was very short and contained mainly minor items and cleaning. In other words, a zero defects building was substantially achieved.

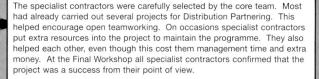

the seven pillars of partnering

A guide to second generation partnering

How BAA's Partnering strategy developed

BAA has a large and diverse construction programme.
The company needed to adopt best practice design and management in all its activities to be globally competitive. The head of BAA, Sir John Egan, came from the car industry to lead the necessary changes.
He set a tough target for construction costs.
Initially many different and largely uncoordinated initiatives were undertaken in parallel. Partnering with consultants, contractors and suppliers was one of these initiatives.

The Pavement Team was given the task of speeding up the development of partnering methods. This emerged as a particularly successful initiative and as a good model of Second Generation Strategic Partnering. Performance improvement took a year to begin to emerge but is now approaching a reduction in costs of 30%.

See overleaf for the journey...

How BAA's Property Strategy Developed

THE BACKGROUND

When Sir John Egan became BAA's Chief Executive in 1990 he quickly recognised that the organisation's construction costs had to be substantially lower if BAA was to be able to compete on the international stage. He set an ambitious target of cutting costs by up to 50%. For this to happen he recognised that BAA would need to change itself internally and change the way the rest of the construction industry works.

THE INITIAL VISION

Initially the changes were expressed as a strategic vision to be pursued through separate initiatives including Strategic Partnering with key suppliers, training to develop teambuilding skills, process analysis and re-engineering, actions aimed directly at cost cutting, value engineering the technology of BAA's buildings and other facilities, and exploiting IT in design, engineering and management processes.

THE STRATEGY FOR CHANGING THE CULTURE

A carefully controlled two-stage Change Process was set up. The First Stage provided procedures for promoting ideas for change, collecting them, and for researching, testing and evaluating the most promising ideas. The second stage guided the implementation and monitored the impact of successful ideas.

IDENTIFYING GOOD SUPPLIERS

To meet EU procurement regulations BAA created five year framework agreements with key consultants, contractors and suppliers. The framework selection process was very thorough and involved the use of detailed questionnaires and structured interviews to select people that BAA felt it would work with efficiently. Final selection was based on a points system of which only 40% related to cost. The careful selection has paid dividends with many highly productive partnering relationships developing. An issue that BAA is now beginning to consider is how the next round of framework agreements should be organised. BAA wants to ensure that carefully built up experience is not thrown away but at the same time it is keen to give every chance to new suppliers able to make an even better contribution.

DEALING WITH MONEY

BAA decided that it was important to address money issues head on. In the past traditional contract arrangements meant that BAA carried some risks and its contractors carried others. This approach also meant that everyone wasted time and resources arguing over blame and liability. The first step was to use a target cost approach in which savings (or extra costs) were shared with contractors. This helped teams to work together, but BAA discovered that they often resorted to their old adversarial habits if they had to renegotiate targets when work was changed. A new approach, being trialled from 1997, goes further in removing money worries. The aim is for contractors to be paid their actual costs plus a fair profit and fixed overhead fee. Partnering teams now concentrate on managing risks. BAA pay for all work and the team concentrates on finding the most cost effective answers to the risks that actually occur. Experience to date shows that it is more efficient and better for everyone when BAA shoulders a fair proportion of the cost risk. Teams work hard to set the lowest possible target, manage the risks and then look for even more savings. Everyone concentrates on doing work in the most efficient way. Driving out waste has become a key motivating force and everyone benefits.

WORKING TOGETHER TO IMPROVE PROCESSES

Initially teams were assembled project by project from approved framework consultants and contractors. BAA now recognises that it takes time to build trust, to learn better ways of working and then apply and improve them. So, as far as possible, work is now organised to keep teams together. Joint working has given BAA staff a commitment to the success of its framework suppliers as they too are striving to provide a reliable annual turnover, consistent profits, and cover fixed overheads. BAA expect in return that its own budgets and completion dates will be met. This is producing win:win attitudes. Work is underway to streamline the BAA approvals processes. Having everyone on board at the start of projects makes it possible to get earlier approvals as they are based on real costs. Another aim is to integrate cost monitoring systems so as to cut out the duplication of one quantity surveyor checking another surveyor's work. The aim is to use one open book system that produces figures everyone can trust. One expected benefit is that cost reporting will be more honest so any problems are identified and tackled earlier.

BAA's Pavement Team

INTRODUCTION

BAA's new runway and apron (or 'pavements') construction work is being undertaken via a Strategic Partnering arrangement between BAA and Amec. It is run by a single organisation formed by staff drawn from both businesses. The technology involved in pavement work is relatively simple and BAA has a regular programme of work so it can provide continuity.

CHANGING ATTITUDES

The team has learned that partnering means different objectives have to be reconciled. For example, BAA wants construction work done at night when there are no flights. It also wants lower construction costs. Amec wants profitable repeat business and a satisfied customer. By 1997 BAA and Amec's staff clearly understood these different goals and were working together as a seamless team in a 'virtual' company. BAA's staff have learned about the realities of construction and the way that costs are incurred on site. Designers in particular have learned the benefits of having contractors on board from the outset. They accept that they can produce better designs earlier by thinking about buildability on the drawing board. Amec staff have learned about the complexity of client organisations. More interestingly they have become aware of their own lack of training in well established management techniques – for example not knowing the principles of running meetings efficiently. A fundamental change for Amec staff is that they are now more proactive in looking for new construction opportunities that fit in with BAA's business plans.

STRATEGY MEMBERSHIP EQUITY INTEGRATION

PARTNE

FINANCIAL ARRANGEMENTS

Initially the money arrangements were based on a gain share:pain share deal in which a target cost was agreed and the contractor:

- received 75% of any savings achieved that were more than 20% below the target
- received 50% of savings between 0% and 20% below the target
- paid 75% of extra costs between 0% and 20% above the target
- paid 100% of any extra costs where they overshot the target budget by 20% or more.

This approach was used from 1995 to 1997, but it led to arguments about how the target should be adjusted when changes occurred. A survey showed that the quantity surveyors were spending 30% of their time negotiating changes to the target and this was not seen as being very productive work. A new approach based on Amec being paid a sum to cover profit and fixed overheads plus its direct costs was introduced in mid-1997. In order to make this approach work Amec had to improve its cost recording systems. Previously its aim had been to maximise profit, which did not require a precise allocation of costs. It now has a better understanding of how money is being spent and the new system also provides a much more reliable guide in the search for savings.

WORKING METHODS

Construction planning is now taken much more seriously with the whole team involved earlier and better data available on standards, times and productivity. The plan is now consistently worked to, and does not have to be re-thought as the work proceeds. There are fewer mistakes, subcontractors start their work in the right place and work in a planned sequence. As a result only half the number of planners are needed for the pavement projects. The management of the pre-construction work is more difficult than on site work and there is more scope for improvement in the early stages. Amec is now working with its client to change BAA's approval procedures so that decisions are taken earlier and the team can get on with its work in greater confidence.

TRUSTING THE CONTRACTOR

A good example of the way construction work can be influenced by partnering is that historically BAA staff responsible for 'airside' operations have tended not to trust contractors. They have therefore set onerous restrictions on where, when and how they were allowed to work. By working in co-operation with the operations staff, Amec has proved that it can work responsibly. As a result the restrictions have been relaxed so that Amec is allowed to work closer to aeroplanes and finish work closer to the first landings of the day.

STANDARD SPECIFICATIONS

There have been significant reductions in the amount of paper needed for each project. For example, BAA has a standard specification for pavement work comprising some 300 pages. Under the previous one-off arrangements a great deal of time was spent customising it for each individual project. Now Amec holds a copy of the standard and individual project documents include just three or four pages of project specific items.

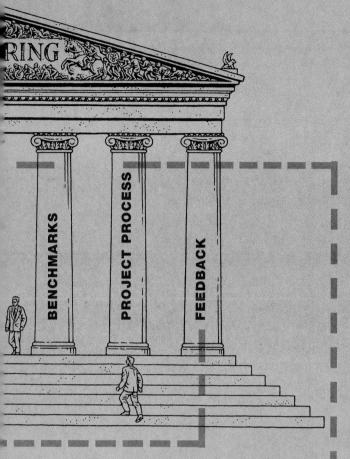

BENCHMARKS
PROJECT PROCESS
FEEDBACK

A SLOW BEGINNING LEADING TO A FLOW OF BENEFITS

he benefits are beginning to be apparent after a slow start largely caused by he framework selection process taking a long time to complete. In the early ays of the arrangement (1995) people were uncertain how things were upposed to work and, perhaps as a result, did not trust each other. Work as rushed with little planning being done. The main achievement in the first ear was to begin teambuilding. The team began to undertake process nalysis at the start of 1996. At about the same time formal performance easurements were established. As a result the work was better planned, arget prices and programmes were steadily reduced and targets were chieved more reliably. During 1996 costs fell by 8.5% and programmes ere reduced by an average of 12 weeks.

ACHIEVING CONTINUOUS IMPROVEMENT

In 1997 these improvements became even more marked. Not only are target costs reducing, the team is now consistently delivering costs below the agreed targets. Overall costs fell by 15% in real terms between 1995 and 1997.

There is a general feeling in the team that it now knows the real costs of pavement work and where waste still exists. The team believes that there is scope for continued improvement for at least the next five years.

The speed of construction has also improved with projects now completed 25 to 30% quicker. Targets are now tougher, but are being met more reliably. Prior to the pavement team being set up, 30% of projects had extensions of time. In 1996 only 20% needed extensions and in 1997 every project met its completion date.

STANDARD DRAWINGS

he team has made considerable progress in developing effective standard rawings. The standards now comprise 200 civils and 30 electrics drawings nd these are used for 80% of all work. There is a proper control system in lace so that only the current version of the drawings can be used. It is now ccepted that improvements to standards must be identified at the concept tage when there is time to analyse the consequences and plan the work roperly. Good ideas that occur later go into the 'ideas bank' to be onsidered for subsequent projects.

the seven pillars of partnering

A guide to second generation partnering

How Rover's Partnering strategy developed

Rover's new Group Design & Engineering Centre (GDEC) houses its car designers and engineers, and was designed and produced using the same methods as the company uses for the design of new cars. These methods are based on Honda's design and management approach and, like all Japanese methods, depend on long-term relationships.

Rover had to work out how the design of cars could be modified and applied to construction. The importance of GDEC is that it succeeded and in doing so achieved close to 40% reductions in cost and time over traditional methods.

All the partnering pillars are in place and the Rover team is now working together to revolutionise the way the building industry works.

See overleaf for the journey...

The Rover Group's Road to Partnering

THE BACKGROUND

In the early to mid 1980's Rover became increasingly dissatisfied with the traditional way the car industry worked because it resulted in a tough adversarial approach with a strong emphasis on lowest costs based on a given design, multiple suppliers and competitive tendering. When Rover linked up with Honda in the late 1980's, Honda instilled in the company a new emphasis on product quality and helped Rover recognise that it needed to respond faster in rapidly changing markets.

ADOPTION OF NEW MANAGEMENT PRACTICES

New management practices such as Total Quality Management, Just-In-Time and Continuous Improvement were adopted by Rover. These encouraged buyers and suppliers to cooperate in partnering arrangements to boost performance by analysing and improving their joint processes. The initiatives were initially resisted by car designers, who were more interested in engineering than in efficiency. The new practices also resulted in a new method of purchasing which evolved from a Honda system called Effective Cost Management (ECM). This encourages business awareness down to the engineering level, so that designers can see the benefits of better added value designs. The ECM approach empowered engineers and others to innovate and search out the best possible answers within a fixed budget. The Purchasing Department helped the engineers really understand their own processes so they could find systematic improvements. The ECM approach recognised that profit depends on the quality of people so there was a need for re-training the workers at all levels.

EFFECTIVE COST MANAGEMENT APPLIED TO BUILDING

When Rover built the new Land Rover Discovery facility and a new production line for the Rover 800 in Cowley this change in culture led to increased cooperation between Purchasing, Manufacturing, Engineering and Finance Departments. The team worked to develop best solutions with a reduced number of suppliers. Both the Purchasing and Engineering teams recognised the traditional basis of procurement for buildings was unacceptable so they decided to select sole suppliers and procure future buildings based on the ECM approach. The team that was established to introduce ECM to building procurement included representatives from Purchasing, Engineering, Finance, Customers and Suppliers. Their goal was to break the mould in the industry and to enjoy themselves and have a better quality of life while they did it!

PRODUCING A BUILDING LIKE A MANUFACTURED PRODUCT

The new Group Design and Engineering Centre (GDEC) project was needed to re-house Rover's car designers and engineers at Gaydon. Mike Stevens, Rover's project manager for GDEC, was determined to set new standards of value for money for Rover. So from the outset it was proposed to make this a unique example of a building produced as if it were a manufactured product.

INTERNAL CORE TEAM AND BUDGET ESTABLISHED

Mike's internal core team was made up of Users representatives, Facilities Managers and Engineers, the Finance Department, the Purchasing Department and Yeoman & Edwards, an independent quantity surveyor who advised on cost control. Ian Pocock from Yeoman & Edwards emerged as a key member of the core team, continually using the cost plan to set challenging targets and chairing most core team meetings. The internal core team began by setting an initial budget of £12m, which was based on Rover's standards as they applied in the early 1990's. The philosophy then was not to spend money on anything that did not directly contribute to building cars and the target of £12m represented a very basic building.

POTENTIAL CONTRACTORS IDENTIFIED

A rigorous selection process was used to assess 35 potential contractors. This looked at each firms' financial viability, technical experience, quality levels, staff attitudes and commercial approach. SDC, which had worked with Rover for 20 years, was among the four firms shortlisted to make a presentation on what it could do for Rover based on some drawings of a new semi-anechoic test chamber, produced by consulting engineers, Rolton. These showed a small building with a sophisticated structure and services. SDC's team included Rolton and other design consultants with experience of the car industry. Although SDC's cost was the highest, it included a list of potential savings based on careful consideration of Rover's needs. For Rover, cost was not a key issue; it was looking for technical competence, cooperation and teamwork, an ability to live with changes and personalities it could partner with.

THE PROJECT VISION

Rover's new Group Design & Engineering Centre (GDEC) began with a very broad general objective to re-house the company's car designers and engineers in a state of the art facility on a new site at Gaydon. The project had to be flexible because Rover's business was in a state of rapid change. Rover's car designers and engineers had to learn how the new building could help them get the best out of new technologies that were emerging. This meant that the process of designing the building also involved the users in a learning process. Guiding this approach was a clear vision of the building. Mike Stevens, Rover's project manager, and Terry Lee, the concept architect, spent four months visiting buildings and talking to car designers around the world in an intense debate about the brief for the new building. They then brought the vision alive by using analogies and metaphors. They described GDEC as having the style of a Rover 600, the fun of a Mini and the robust character of a Land Rover. This vision became a set of criteria, values and ideas about style and quality that guided the team in its joint development of the building that was eventually constructed. GDEC began on site in May 1994 even though at that time Rover did not know how many people would be accommodated in it, nor the future technologies it might use in designing cars. This meant that everything had to be kept fluid and that future flexibility in working practices within the building would also be needed. However, the budget was fixed at £24.5m.

SELECTING THE TEAM

The most important feature of the project was that it applied best practice car design methods based on partnering to a building. The key to this was to select individuals and firms likely to work as a team in a relentless search for the best possible design decisions.

Rover selected the personnel for GDEC carefully so as to get a rich mix of knowledge in a single highly motivated team. The aim was to find experts in every important aspect of the use, design and construction of buildings. It also wanted a team with the maturity to cooperate with each other in meeting its overall objectives for the project. These skills had to be applied at three distinct levels.

- **Top Management Leadership**
  This is where the overall leadership of the project and the mandate for using partnering to give a new way of working had to be provided. In a mould breaking project such as GDEC, tough, experienced leadership was essential from the core team.

- **Technical Design and Management**
  The second level of skills was provided by the technical designers and managers. On GDEC, this level needed to be very strong to cope with the innovation and creativity that the core team demanded. This was achieved by selecting firms that brought very experienced professional designers and managers into the team and ensuring that they had every opportunity to communicate effectively.

- **Technical Specialists**
  The third level of skills came from the specialists who worked on the individual elements. Many of these contractors were crucial to the project's success as Rover had insisted that every aspect of the building should be debated and questioned in a search for the best possible answers.

DEVELOPING PARTNERING ATTITUDES

The steelwork contractors for Rover's Group Design & Engineering Centre (GDEC) had no experience of Partnering before the project.

Through a series of informal discussions and formal presentations, Conder was selected to join in Partnering with the rest of the GDEC team. The arrangement was that its overheads and profits were agreed on the basis of its lump sum bid.

Bill Nicholson, Conder's Managing Director, had to carefully select the team to cope with this new way of working.

Having selected his team, he addressed an initial meeting of his key people to describe Partnering and the open book approach he was going to adopt. Initially this was quite daunting for the team, and Bill had to continually reinforce the message. This took time, but after about eight weeks everyone was clearly very committed as they recognised that they did not have to worry about unnecessary, non-value adding activities.

SORTING OUT THE MONEY

On GDEC the client agreed to pay everyone an agreed profit and overhead percentage plus their properly incurred direct costs. This removed concerns over money and allowed everyone to concentrate on making their best and fullest contribution. As one of the team said: "Take money fears out of the equation and people start producing remarkable results."

Payments were made on the basis of each firm's own cost records. The quantity surveyors audited the process and agreed each firm's figures. This ensured that the costs claimed were fair.

For Rover it was vital that GDEC was produced within budget. An important part of Rover's approach for achieving this was making it a matter of pride for the whole project team that they understood, accepted and stayed within the agreed cost plan. This was achieved at a special meeting of the whole team, including Rover's staff who were involved with the project. At the end of the meeting everyone accepted personal responsibility for achieving the budget.

OPEN BOOK ACCOUNTING

The firms involved in the team worked on a basis of genuine equality and recognised that everyone was a potential source of solutions to design problems. The firms also worked on an open book basis. They were all guaranteed their normal profit and paid their costs. Rover's project manager said: "We seek to develop a supplier company's business alongside ours so we become mutually profitable and the relationship is self-supporting."

A key motivating factor for the project team was the assurance of further work if it did a good job. The other main motivator was the satisfaction from a job well done. Rover believes that if it has picked the best available firms it should endeavour to keep working with them. Should something go wrong, the firms are expected to put it right without blame being ascribed. As Rover's project manager says: "If they were the best team before a mistake is made, they are still the best team afterwards."

STRATEGY MEMBERSHIP EQUITY INTEGRATION

PARTNE

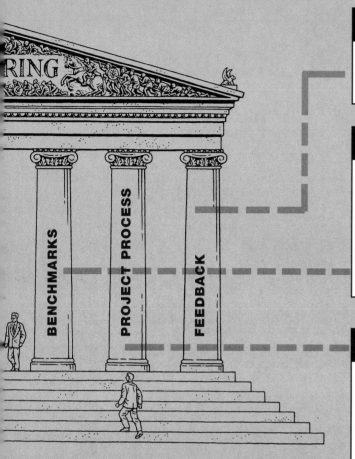

3

BENCHMARKS

PROJECT PROCESS

FEEDBACK

POST-PROJECT: THE MOVE INTO THIRD GENERATION PARTNERING

Rolton and a group of the other companies involved with GDEC are now partnering to actively market their joint expertise to others in the car industry. This is significant because the firms are deliberately attempting to build a business on the back of a very successful project and this approach is therefore leading to Third Generation Partnering.

DELIVERY

GDEC embodies Rover values, is well engineered, looks good and is British in style. It also includes some interesting innovations in building technology. Most importantly the building helps the users work more effectively. They have quickly learnt how to use GDEC's open plan offices. They find that they can work independently when they need to without needless interruptions, yet impromptu meetings are much more effective than ever before. This has happened because the GDEC users have adopted the discipline of interrupting one another only if they have something important to discuss. GDEC is also a remarkable building because despite a very high level of change from the client, it was completed to meet Rover's rigid time and budget criteria. More than this, the building was almost 40% cheaper and was occupied 12 months earlier than would have been possible with traditional JCT methods.

FLEXIBLE PROCESSES IN ACTION

GDEC provides a world class car design facility by exploiting methods developed in the Japanese car industry and brought to Rover through its link with Honda. To provide this approach Rover used simultaneous engineering to deal with a design that was constantly changing. During the project BMW acquired Rover and made substantial changes to the new building. For example a £1.4m entrance and atrium and an extra storey were added to part of the building. Steelwork in the areas affected had already been erected. This meant a hole had to be left for the entrance and atrium, which were added later. The exact nature of these changes were not decided all at once but emerged gradually over several months while design and construction were both well underway and the steel structure was substantially complete. Partnering made it possible for the team to absorb these changes without claims or delays. BMW totally supported the view that the rate of change in Rover's markets was unlikely to slow down, so the building itself was designed to be flexible. Spaces are designed to be used in many different ways, and the steel structure has already proved capable of accommodating change and extension. Another example was that the cladding the team originally planned to use did not match the agreed quality vision. This problem arose at an awkward time just as BMW was buying Rover. As a result it was difficult to get decisions taken by the client. The team dealt with this by putting up a rainscreen so it could take the cladding off the critical path. The new system improved the fire safety but created a substantial overspend which could have potentially affected the programme and the budget significantly. However the team worked together to modify the steelwork and absorb all the additional costs from savings achieved elsewhere.

COOPERATING IN THE TEAM

A key to effective decision making on the GDEC project was the use of a large open plan project office which housed everyone involved in making design decisions. Thus the main contractor, consultants, specialists and the quantity surveyor all worked as one integrated team. The normal style of decision making was for meetings to take place in the project office as they were needed. These took place around a white board on which decisions were recorded. At the end of the meeting everyone was given a photocopy of the white board, and the board would be left as a public record of the decisions until it was needed for another meeting. In this way everyone in the project team had the opportunity to tune into all the decisions in an almost subliminal manner. In a deep, fundamental sense, the open plan office created an open approach to communication and control. In a project characterised by change, it was essential to be able to accommodate change as a normal part of everyday work. The unstructured approach of concentrating on solving problems by bringing together everyone who might have a contribution to make provided the flexibility needed. A key strategy in the decision making approach was to cut out the use of paper. Mike Stevens believes that having selected firms that are competent, there is no value in giving them written instructions. Everyone was responsible and had the opportunity to join in decision making. And once something was decided, everyone was expected to concentrate on making the decision work as well as possible.

COST, TIME AND QUALITY CONTROL

A very tough cost control and cost audit system was imposed backed up by relentless pressure from the client to look for the best possible value. This forced the core team to question every element of the project in the search for savings. The key cost control document was the quantity surveyors' (Yeoman & Edwards) Cost Detail Tracking Sheet which monitored the latest indicated cost. Cost Tracking was kept up-to-date and the current position reported to the core team Meeting every two weeks. The most interesting feature of the Cost Tracking Sheet was its identification of cost risks and opportunities. Everyone in the project team had a responsibility for identifying these items. The core team discussed all the items listed in the summary of cost risks and opportunities at its meetings. As decisions were made their impact was incorporated in the statements of latest indicated cost. Time control was based on fixed milestones that were defined as they were reached in terms of the information needed to avoid delaying the project. This meant that decisions were made only when they were absolutely necessary. The milestones required a brisk though not fast pace of work. This allowed the project team time to search for good designs without continuing beyond the point of diminishing returns. To ensure that all the milestones were met, the team made sure an alternative solution that used a known technology was available if no better design could be found. Quality control for every aspect was in the hands of the people doing the work. This is because the best practice from all modern industries shows that workers must be given responsibility for the quality of their own work if defects are to be eliminated. Mike Stevens takes the view that this is the only way to eliminate defects from building work.

COOPERATING DOWN THE SUPPLY CHAIN

The specialist contractors used on Rover's Group Design and Engineering Centre (GDEC) project were encouraged to shop around to get the best prices from their own suppliers, and this produced significant savings. Roltons, Rover's services designers, produced designs and equipment specifications and the specialist contractors were then asked to produce their most cost effective proposals. These were reviewed by Roltons, SDC (the main contractors) and Rover's facilities managers and maintenance staff. The savings achieved were dramatic - for example, the air handling units were bought for a total of £169,000 against the earlier cheapest quotation of £225,000.

the seven pillars of partnering

A guide to second
generation partnering

How Esso's Partnering strategy developed

The development of Esso's pan-European standard service station shop represents an important example of manufacturing based Third Generation Partnering. Esso has worked through a long process of continuous improvement since at least the mid-1980s. Successive targets were set for improvements in quality, time and then cost.

In the UK serial contracting had been used to achieve these improvements. By the early 1990s performance had been pushed as far as it would go as long as traditional construction approaches were used.

Esso's demand in the UK market was too small to make prefabrication viable. A task force based in the UK was set up to explore the possibility of using other forms of construction. This has led to the setting up of pan-European Strategic Partnering arrangements with just two suppliers. The approach is now being applied world-wide.

The use of prefabrication has halved construction time, delivered more reliable quality and achieved cost reductions of as much as 60%.

See overleaf for the journey...

How Esso's Construction Strategy Developed

HOW ESSO'S ROAD TO PARTNERING DEVELOPED

By the mid 1980s Esso's service stations had a clear corporate image world-wide. They were produced to industry norms of cost and time. Nevertheless the company set about systematically improving them by concentrating innovations successively on quality, time and then cost. This was done in the individual affiliates (countries). In the UK, Esso's use of serial contracting had demonstrated the benefits of long-term relationships and the use of standard designs.

THE BACKGROUND

Since the 1980's Esso has used traditional forms of construction and serial contracting as the main way of procuring its service stations in the UK. This approach helped ensure they were built quickly and to reliable quality standards. But there were clear limits to further improvement. Firstly, Esso's annual budgeting procedures meant that projects could only begin on site after a host of internal and external approvals had been obtained so contractors were not provided with a steady stream of work. Secondly, there was a competitive band of specialist contractors serving this niche market, so the effects of serial contracting were limited. Construction costs on schemes procured this way were therefore very similar to those produced from one-off tendering.

TIME FOR A STEP CHANGE

By the mid 1990s Esso had come to the conclusion that serial contracting, while it had delivered many benefits over the last decade, was unlikely to produce further big improvements in performance as long as it continued using traditional construction. Mindful of the stiff competition it faced from other petrol retailers, especially the big supermarket chains, Esso commissioned a study of 20 companies so it could benchmark its performance. This concluded that there was still scope for considerably improving performance and it also suggested that this step change could be delivered by moving to prefabrication techniques.

THE BLUE RIBBON TASK FORCE

The Blue Ribbon Task Force was set up in 1994 by Exxon Company International (ECI) to focus on cutting service station costs. It included representatives from various affliliates and outside consultants. Its targets were to save 5-10% by eliminating bad practice, to then focus on using current best practice to double these savings up to 10-20%, and to exploit innovative solutions to increase the overall savings to 20-30%. The goal of achieving these targets was initially tackled through a European Task Force led by Simon Stocks, an engineer from Esso UK. Simon was appointed to head the Task Force in part because Esso's UK operations were among the best in Europe in achieving cost and time reductions. Each European affiliate was set targets which added up to a predicted overall saving of £30m.At the same time there was to be no reduction in the quality of the end product as perceived by Esso's customers.

DEVELOPING A VISION

A vision site was designed and built using traditional construction. It tried out many new ideas in order to decide which could be developed further in the layout and design of future service stations.

STANDARD BUILDINGS

Early in 1994 Esso representatives from the European affiliates began to use Partnering to exploit their joint purchasing power and develop standardised buildings. Throughout this work there was a strong focus on the use of modular buildings and various design modifications were accepted to facilitate the use of prefabrication techniques.

Esso's Standard Shop

BACKGROUND

The development of the standard shop began by benchmarking and value engineering current best practice. Esso concentrated on getting costs down by challenging existing norms. This covered things like the number of bathrooms that should be provided, the use of glazed wall tiles, the need for high quality finishes in store rooms and the size of store rooms.

MODULAR BUILDING TRIALS

In 1995 the UK affiliate of Esso developed a modular prefabricated approach and the first prototypes were built in the UK and Germany. All of the European members were encouraged to try prototype prefabricated approaches. In total 25 shops were constructed by eight different suppliers using various mixes of modular and flat pack solutions. These trials confirmed that the best answer for the shop element was to use prefabrication as it was quicker and safer on site and the quality was as good as traditional. There were initial concerns that the modular structures would not feel like real buildings but it is now recognised that quality aspects are determined by design. Initially the cost was equal to traditional but it was accepted that the buying power of Esso across Europe should see costs reducing rapidly.

SELECTING FIRMS TO PREFABRICATE THE SHOPS

Bids were invited for a prefabricated shop for the whole of Europe (14 countries). In the first phase of the bidding process potential suppliers were asked to price two different layouts. Both comprised modules plus flat pack infill elements. One shop was to be built to UK standards and the other to German standards. Quality was defined in the bid documents as being fit for purpose. The firms were asked to bid for one year for whatever geographical area of Europe they were confident they could supply and they were given seven weeks to submit their prices. Seventeen bids were received in January 1997 and these were evaluated for each of the two layouts in each of the countries. After a careful evaluation of the bids, two firms were selected.

SUPPLYING EUROPE WITH EVEN BETTER VALUE

The two successful firms were Rousseau Stewing and General Electric Capital Modular Space. In the second phase of the bidding process each company was invited to meet country specific layouts and local regulations. The firms had to demonstrate that they had maintained the same price level as in their earlier bids. The result was that both suppliers achieved the lowest price in about half the countries and between them they provided the lowest price for 26 of the 28 country:layout combinations. They were only marginally more expensive in the other two cases. The overall price range was from $125,000 to $210,000 depending on the layout, etc. There were big differences between some countries mainly due to the location of factories and the resulting differences in transport costs.

PARTNE

STRATEGY

MEMBERSHIP

EQUITY

INTEGRATION

Esso's use of modular buildings has cut cost by up to 60%

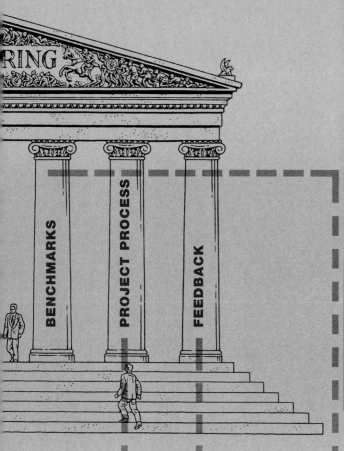

BENCHMARKS · PROJECT PROCESS · FEEDBACK

STANDARDISED SOLUTION WITH LOCAL VARIETY

From the start Esso's Retail Engineering Skills Centre's aims were to standardise the layouts and meet national regulations. So, based on their country specific bids, both suppliers worked through partnering arrangements to agree the details of their product with Esso's team in each of the countries. The result was a single solution applicable to the whole of Europe, plus a range of optional extras. Esso's team in each country has been given a full description of its country specific solution from each of the two firms in a pack that contains the agreed standard layout, a pricing document and the options available. An element of competition has been retained in each country by allowing both companies to be suppliers and leaving it to the company in each country to decide which it uses. There will need to be a minimum call up of shops from each supplier in order to cover their fixed costs. It is possible, if one supplier gets most of the orders, that the Skill Centre will need to intervene and request countries to use the other supplier. This is unlikely to happen because of the differences in prices in individual countries. An on-going part of the partnering process is for RESC to agree with the suppliers their contribution to the improvement of their product and service. The aim is to ensure that both firms are seriously working with Esso to achieve continuous improvements to their joint performance.

ACHIEVING CONTINUOUS IMPROVEMENT

The development of the standard shop shows that by organising demand Esso has made it possible for its two suppliers to set up sophisticated factories to manufacture standard buildings. This is merely the beginning in achieving the steady continuous improvement which is the hallmark of modern industry. At the end of each year, RESC benchmarks the average cost of each country's standard service stations versus their old traditional approach. Taking 1994 as the base year, the total savings by mid 1997 were:

■ 15-25% in France/Benelux/UK

■ 50-60% in Germany and Switzerland

In some countries like Italy and Finland, only minor savings have been achieved. However it should be pointed out that Italy has been and still is the "leader" in terms of absolute cost. The benchmarks are used by RESC to work in cooperation with the two suppliers and ensure that they continue to be the source of ideas for further major economies so that the continuous improvements in performance are maintained.

the seven pillars of partnering

A guide to second
generation partnering

Second Generation

Pillars of Partnering

4

Second Generation Partnering takes place when a client decides to work with construction firms in a focused strategic way on more than one project, or some continuing construction activity such as maintenance or facilities management. It is also used effectively on very large projects – so called mega-projects, that comprise a series of normal 'projects' which together provide a single facility.

Having agreed to Partner the whole team examines every aspect of project work to improve their overall performance. Second Generation Partnering usually works through a Strategic Team.

Many Second Generation Partnering arrangements set up task forces to undertake long-term research and development that would be difficult to implement on an individual project.

At its best, Second Generation Partnering ensures that all the industry parties act in the best interests of the client; and the client acts in the best interests of the industry firms. These cooperative behaviours are helped by each party appointing a Partnering Champion.

The seven pillars of Second Generation Partnering

provide a framework that encapsulate the main practical lessons learnt from the case studies. Each pillar represents a distinct set of management actions that provide an essential element of successful partnering. The full benefits of partnering are driven by the explicit development of a strategy which is put into effect by strategic task forces that develop specific initiatives, and individual projects. This is the first Pillar and it provides the overall direction for the next five pillars. The middle five pillars guide the direct work that flows from the agreed strategy. In total they provide the methods, standards, systems, procedures and culture needed to support cooperative ways of working. In doing this they ensure that the Strategic Team has the capacity and will to seek continuous improvements in the performance of their individual projects.

STRATEGIC TEAMS

Strategic Teams include a senior representative of all the firms that have agreed to Partner together and they are responsible for the overall direction of Second Generation Partnering organisations.

The members of the Strategic Team need to have the authority to commit their own firm to jointly agreed actions. Where they are the chief executive, as is common in the building industry, this raises no problems. If not they must have the confidence of their chief executive.

The principle role of the Strategic Team is to plan long-term for continuous, measurable improvements in project performance.

Strategic Teams work through workshops held at regular intervals – usually every month or quarter. Many strategic workshops use an independent facilitator.

Workshops are provided with feedback on the performance of current projects. They also have reports from strategic task forces on specific initiatives that have been set in train or new technological or market developments. They focus on recurring problems and look for new opportunities.

In the early stages of a Second Generation Partnering arrangement workshops deal with the issues discussed in the Equity and Integration Pillars – both of which are discussed in detail later in this Chapter – to ensure that the Strategic Partnering organisation becomes ever more tightly integrated and this is then reflected in the financial arrangements that guide their work.

When a workshop identifies the need for action, a strategic task force may be launched or the team will identify a project that can be used to put the actions into effect. In either case they make sure that the objectives are clear and adequate resources are available. They also set up the means by which the results will be reported to them.

The Strategic Team normally appoints people to form the core team on individual projects, sets their objectives and ensures that each of them is employed on terms that empower them to do their best work in the interests of the project. A further important part of their work is establishing the standards and procedures the core teams will use.

It is important that the firms represented on a Strategic Team are committed to investing long-term in continuously improving their performance. To help ensure this the performance of project teams and all the firms involved is evaluated by the Strategic Team. These evaluations are used to guide decisions about appointments and in setting objectives on future projects.

The strategic evaluation of firms is designed to encourage core teams to concentrate on doing their best possible work on the current project. All the preferred firms are evaluated, including consultants, main contractors and specialist contractors. Evaluation is based on performance over all the projects the firm has worked on in the period under consideration – usually 12 months. Firms that do not meet the performance evaluation criteria are helped with advice about how to improve. The penalty for continued non-performance is less work accompanied by more direct help. But if performance does not improve, the firm risks getting no more work. In this way the Strategic Team identify preferred firms that - as far as possible – can be used on all projects.

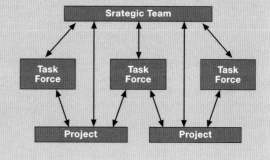

All this is managed with the aid of the seventh pillar which deals with feedback from strategic task forces and project processes. This turns the strategic process into a controlled system by providing objective measures of performance to guide the ongoing development of the overall strategy.

All seven pillars need regular attention for Second Generation Partnering to deliver its full benefits. Together they provide the basis for individual projects to be carried out efficiently yet enable the Strategic Team to search systematically for ever better designs and ways of working.

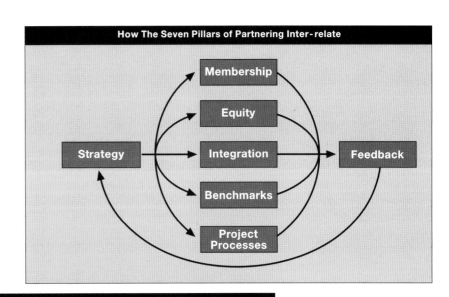

How The Seven Pillars of Partnering Inter-relate

PARTNERING CHAMPIONS

A partnering champion is committed to the concept of Partnering and is responsible for ensuring his or her organisation understands and implements partnering as widely as possible. They should be a senior manager who has the confidence of the whole organisation – from the chief executive to people at the workface. The champion should also have a track record of managing change. The champion must understand that cooperation is the best way of working. They need lots of energy to take on new initiatives and they must be willing to take risks. The champion needs to understand how the organisation works and how things get done. They need to know the best ways of getting support for new initiatives and if necessary, they must be willing to turn the organisation on its head. It follows that the champion needs to be a negotiator who enjoys what they do and knows how to get other people excited about new ideas.

Getting Started

The first action of the champion must be to fully understand Partnering. Then they must understand the strategic objectives, what they mean for their own organisation and the potential benefits.

Champions manage communications about partnering inside their own organisation so they can build support for its aims, attitudes and behaviours.

It is important that the champion does not try to impose their own ideas about the best approach. The most effective approach is one of coaching by asking questions in ways that encourage everyone to join in discussions and then 'buy in' to decisions.

It needs to be recognised that groups – not individuals – change organisations. The champion needs to find like minds to assist them and form a company-wide network. In setting up the network the following three types of people are needed:

- Carriers to help the champion carry the message of Partnering. These are people who share the vision, can be trusted and will take risks.

- Gatekeepers to help the champion get agreement to new ways of working. These

people know how the organisation really works. They are often the 'politicians' of the company – people who know how to open or close gates and can guide the champion in getting approvals.

- Experts to help the champion fully understand Partnering. These could be a partnering facilitator, partnering consultant or experts in process analysis.

When a strategy involves new ways of working champions need to create pressure for change and establish a clear shared vision, values and behaviours. They then need to analyse what will happen that will be different. They also need a plan to deal with the inevitable reactions.

Tactics

In putting the strategy into effect the champion should continually ask for more. They should push the carriers really hard, work at building cooperative relationships with the gatekeepers and use the experts ruthlessly by constantly picking their brains.

They should build on the experiences of working cooperatively that already exist in their firm. Informal long-term relationships are important in this. Where they exist, efforts should be made to formalise them and move them towards Partnering.

Champions should also seek to ensure that their organisation rewards cooperative behaviour.

Feedback

The champion should ensure that there is good feedback on their organisation's progress towards the adoption of Partnering. They should arrange regular face-to-face discussions with people to assess their views. They should keep the processes of Partnering under review at feedback workshops to ensure that practice is continuously improving. They must ensure that senior management have convincing evidence of the benefits of continuing to support the organisation's use of Partnering.

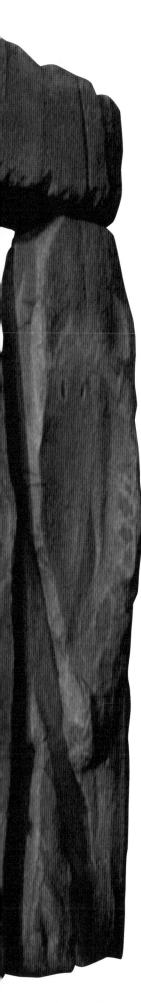

The strategy pillar deals with the need for long-term thinking by the Partnering organisation. It provides the 'brain' in an intelligent controlled system that works through regulated flows of information and decision making. Flowing to the 'brain' is feedback from projects and task forces, while flowing from the 'brain' are strategies and targets.

The strategy pillar represents the broad decisions which set the scene for how the arrangement is going to work. The feedback pillar feeds information about the performance of the Partnering organisations into the strategy pillar. This information is then reviewed, decisions are made and then fed into the middle five pillars to define the parameters within which task forces and project core teams should work.

STRATEGIC PLANNING

General strategic plans are established by the Strategic Team guided by formal R&D and good ideas from all parts of the organisation formed by the Partnering firms. These are elaborated into programmes and operating plans by strategic task forces and project core teams.

COMMITMENT

The strategies need to be supported by all the organisations involved in the Partnering arrangement. This commitment gradually builds up through the experience of working together successfully. It is shaped and guided at workshops that bring the Strategic Team together at frequent intervals. In the early years of a Partnering arrangement, there may need to be monthly meetings to review and guide progress and ensure commitment.

ELEMENTS OF STRATEGY

A clear strategy will improve the probability of success for the Partnering arrangement. The strategy should include:

● The most important goals or objectives to be achieved
● The policies and procedures to guide them
● The major processes to be worked through in order to accomplish the defined goals

MISSION STATEMENT

The starting point should be a mission statement which states what the Partnering organisation wants to have achieved five to ten years in the future. The mission statement reflects what the team is in business to do with specific targets on which all the firms involved can set their sights. It also sets out the long-term mutual objectives of the Partnering firms.

PARTNERING CHARTERS

The overall targets can be expressed in a Partnering Charter which describes the critical success factors for the relationship. The Charter will also set specific performance improvement targets to be achieved through individual projects.

An example of a Partnering Charter

BUSINESS PLANS

The Strategic Team should develop short and long range business plans for the organisation. This planning should not be a one-off activity, but continuous. These objectives need to be mutual and argued through sufficiently to get real commitment. The long-term objectives should be broad brush, within which there are short-term targets which are more focused. The short-term targets establish project teams and task forces' objectives.

The actions needed to implement the agreed strategies should be integrated into a comprehensive plan. This means determining the actions to be taken, the order in which they are to be accomplished; the approach to be taken, such as using a consultant for all of your training or doing it in-house; the resources to be committed and the time to be allocated.

All of these decisions are subject to change – markets, technology, employees and management policies are all likely to evolve.

CONTINUITY

A key issue for the Strategic Team is to decide how it can provide the continuity needed to keep efficient teams together.

RATIONALISING PROCESSES

The key to delivering the strategic benefits is not in looking for similarities in end products but rather in devising common processes. This is how modern manufacturing firms are able to combine volume production with variety in their end products. Firms develop a small number of standardised processes so that teams stay together and then they design products to fit one of their standard processes. Products that do not fit are either not made or subcontracted to a smaller bespoke manufacturer. Construction will succeed in providing the continuity that Second Generation Partnering depends on only if it too concentrates on rationalising its processes.

CONCENTRATION

Real improvements come from concentrating on one aspect of work: for example quality, time, cost, safety, service or value. However, this concentration must not be pushed too far or it will distort the Partnering organisation's work. Managers need to maintain a balance between all the key issues by making progress in one area and then, when significant improvement has been achieved, switching to a new emphasis.

FREEDOM FOR INDIVIDUALS

Strategies that take account of all these principles provide the firms involved with sufficient security to invest in developing and improving their products and processes. But good strategies also provide a degree of freedom for individuals to act on their own initiatives and so deliver that element of surprise which underlies creativity and innovation. Organisations from all walks of life that survive for a very long time combine a firm discipline in sticking to agreed objectives with the freedom for individuals to act on their own initiative. This means living with ambiguities and sometimes accepting that rules can be broken by people dealing with specific situations or opportunities as long as they maintain the best interests of the overall organisation. Strategies that provide both will give building industry firms and their clients the best possible chance of gaining all the benefits that Second Generation Partnering can deliver.

BUSINESS CASE FOR PROJECTS

Strategic Teams put their strategy into practice by altering the way individual projects are managed. The changes need to be considered from the earliest stage of a project.

Individual construction projects depend on the client establishing a business case that justifies investment.

Client organisations often have many divisions or levels involved in establishing the business case for a

Strategy gem - Distribution Partnering

Distribution Partnering has a mission to become acknowledged as the most efficient producer of large distribution facilities in the world. As a result it expects to win a steadily growing share of the European market.

A Strategic Team has been established that includes Gazeley Properties (developers), Chetwood Associates (architects), Edward Roscoe Associates (structural engineers), Kelly Taylor & Associates (services engineers), Simons Group (contractors) W H Stephens & Sons (quantity surveyors) and The University of Reading (research).

It meets every six weeks to review progress on its projects and to discuss reports from task forces set up to tackle specific innovations.

To deliver its mission the team's strategy was to invest in developing Partnering on a series of projects each of which tries out a specific innovation. The savings made on the projects fund the team's investment in innovative Partnering developments.

Distribution Partnering's approach involved Benchmarking the team's performance against the best in Europe to establish specific achievable targets for improvement. The team also recognised that it would have to integrate the partners' IT and CAD systems to create a single virtual' organisation and explore the use of large scale manufactured components and prefabricated elements to achieve substantial reductions in construction costs and timeframes.

As part of its strategy the team recognised that it would have to clearly define the aims and objectives, publicise its results, consciously seek out new innovative solutions and improve efficiency levels, quality control, speed and overall value for money.

new building project and often the business case is produced by people concerned with financial or technical backgrounds and with little or no property or building industry expertise.

Strategic Teams overcome this weakness by involving everyone and ensuring they all have a clear understanding of the client's real needs, and what trade offs between the various objectives are permitted.

It is good practice for project teams to aim to deliver more than the client expects. This is only possible when they really understand the client's business case for the project.

PROJECT OBJECTIVES

The Strategic Team sets the objectives for individual projects. In most cases these objectives will require the project team to apply the currently agreed

The £380m Bluewater project is intended to be Europe's most imaginatively designed regional shopping and leisure centre. At 150,000m^2 (1.6 million ft^2) it will also be the country's largest – equivalent to 19 full sized football pitches. There are many stakeholders in this mega-project. Bluewater will have three major department stores – Marks and Spencer, John Lewis and House of Fraser and their views had to be balanced in forming the project's objectives, as indeed did the interests of the tenants for the 300 other shops.

Lend Lease, the developer of Bluewater, went to considerable lengths to involve local people in the development of the brief for the new centre, so it consciously sought their views and ideas. Focus groups were set up to include older people, young mothers etc to gather positive and negative shopping experiences. As a result of this study some 400 points were collated. Among the many valuable issues were requests to:

- make the car parking bays larger, so that people could get into and out of their cars more easily
- the adoption of the hospitality concept – incorporating a range of initiatives that would treat customers more like guests

Lend Lease is Partnering with Bovis as its Construction Manager. Bovis has fully supported Lend Lease in its drive to develop a project culture which helps establish Bluewater as a project brand dedicated to customer service. Within the project partnering relationships and attitudes are fostered at focus groups and through training. By changing the culture of the industry Bovis aim to give everyone the freedom to take initiatives aimed at finding the best solution, to push out the boundaries of what is possible, and focus on building strengths for the future.

approach while making one or two specific improvements to performance. However, alongside this Second Generation Partnering also seeks radically new answers.

A clear understanding of exactly who is the client can have a big impact on a project's objectives. For example, the need to satisfy funding institutions may limit effective Partnering by imposing constraints on the technical answers and processes that can be used.

Having answered the question 'Who is the client?' the project team should next consider what each stakeholder could get from the project that is exciting, surprising and goes beyond their expectations.

To ensure that all the interests, constraints and opportunities are considered and constantly kept in mind the Strategic Team may insist on including representatives of many organisations at project workshops – from the funding institutions to users, neighbours and environmentalists.

This all helps achieve the twin aims of Second Generation Partnering:

- To carry out projects using the most efficient methods available, and,
- To encourage innovation and creativity.

The Heathrow Express is the first privately funded railway built in the UK since Victorian times. It will link London Paddington with all four terminals at Heathrow Airport. The total journey time will be 15 minutes and the first train is scheduled to run on 1 June 1998. During the early stages workshops were used to ensure that the team fully understood the project's requirements. At these workshops, the client's Managing Director introduced the three key elements of his vision for the project - building a business; creating a world class railway and offering first class customer service. The client's construction director and a representative from the joint venture contracting team would then explain in more detail the overall strategy. There were again three key elements - creating a single team; creating a culture of trust and making the project an enjoyable experience.

They would then explain the project objectives in terms of time, best value, quality and safety. Later external facilitators would ask the team to consider, debate and report in mixed groups – client, consultants, contractors and suppliers – their reactions (both positively and cautionary). Positive reaction would be added to the project culture databank and action plans formulated to overcome any concerns. So far the reaction has been immensely encouraging and supportive. Newsletters, an Information Centre, Supper Nights and monthly Suppliers Club meetings are also used to reinforce the one:team approach.

The membership pillar is concerned with who is involved in a Partnering arrangement. There are two common ways in which Second Generation Partnering is normally set up. Either a client with a regular programme of work decides to adopt Partnering and sets about selecting partners, or a group of firms that have worked together successfully on several projects decide to formalise their relationship.

In either case the criteria should mainly be based on the nature of the work to be undertaken, the interests of the firms involved and their vision of how the Partnering arrangement should develop. This information will determine the kind of firms that should be involved. Once that is settled, a formal selection process should be adopted.

SELECTION PROCESS

Time and resources should be made available for a carefully set out step by step process. Choosing competent partners is crucial to the success of Partnering arrangements. The best solutions usually involve a formal process, which consists of questionnaires, structured interviews, visits to the firms being considered, and informal discussions with the key people likely to be involved in the work.

Second Generation Partnering arrangements should include firms who between them are capable of making a significant improvement in joint performance. This usually requires a range of firms each providing some of the key skills and knowledge. An important decision is whether the arrangement should include just one or more than one firm of each type.

The arrangement chosen will be influenced by the amount of work available and how capital intensive the necessary technologies need to be.

HOW MANY FIRMS?

In deciding how many firms of each kind to involve, it should be remembered that it is not ideal to be locked into a single supplier nor a single customer. The advantages of Partnering with more than one supplier are that it generates more good ideas, there is greater security, and there is an opportunity to use directly relevant benchmarks to ensure that all the suppliers keep searching for improvements. Partnering works well when about 25% of any organisation's business provides continuity of work for the firms involved. This allows several Partnering arrangements to be set up in parallel and so retains the incentives provided by competition. This should not be carried to excess and although some clients can use many contractors and still provide continuity, there is wide agreement that more than three or four dilutes efforts and benefits.

STRUCTURING MEMBERSHIP TO ENCOURAGE REPEAT BUSINESS

Firms are usually attracted to Partnering because it offers greater certainty, more repeat business and increased profits.

An effective way of delivering certainty is for firms to have rolling contracts that provide a minimum call up. Two or three years is common and the minimum call up needs to be at least sufficient for the supplier to cover overhead costs. This approach allows a long-term relationship to be ended but in a manner that gives time for an exclusive or heavily committed firm to look for other markets or other suppliers.

The use of rolling contracts is common in Partnering arrangements that involve facilities management. Traditionally maintenance contracts run for several years with the market being tested every three or five years.

OPEN RELATIONSHIPS

In Partnering it is important for relationships to be open and transparent. This means being open about contract conditions with suppliers and subcontractors so firms 'upstream' can be confident that all the benefits of Partnering will be available 'downstream'.

CERTAINTY FOR CLIENTS

Contractors and consultants don't always recognise that creating certainty is a two-way process. Clients also need to be sure they get better value for money otherwise they may decide to 'test' the market and a rogue bid can then destroy a Partnering relationship. Creating this kind of certainty for clients is best achieved by consultants and contractors measuring their own performance in terms of the contribution it makes to the client's business and then presenting the results to the client's senior management.

SELECTING PROJECT CORE TEAMS

Competition is the right answer when products and services can be fully defined in the tender documents and it is unlikely that these will be changed. Where design has to be discussed and the definition of the required products and services will be produced gradually as the project unfolds, Partnering provides the right approach. It is the most efficient way of organising a human activity that needs interaction, debate, negotiation and joint decisions.

For all these reasons it is often best, for key aspects of projects – such as the conceptual design, the structural elements, the external cladding, the services, etc. – to appoint clusters of firms who have worked together before. Building the project team from such clusters has many efficiency benefits. This is especially the case where the people involved have already worked with the client on similar projects.

The kind of certainty needed for Partnering to flourish requires firms who are prepared to have a longer term view. Partners should be selected based on a broad evaluation of their competence and culture – not just on price. The most highly developed arrangements undertake the evaluation at regular intervals and turn it into a numerical score that is combined with the firm's price in selecting best value. This means that a firm delivering zero defects, working cooperatively with the client in finding innovations that help the client's business, investing heavily in training, and having every prospect of still being in business in ten years time could offer a

higher price than a firm doing none of these things and still be awarded a significant share of the work.

DEVELOPING PARTNERING SKILLS

The research suggests that multi-skilled teams are crucial for partnering to deliver its full benefits. So project core teams need people who are very competent in their own discipline and skilled in communicating their decisions and judgements in terms that other disciplines understand. Consequently architects should be able to talk the language of engineers, construction managers and specialist contractors. The same is true for all the specialist disciplines.

Workers need the ability to learn, to communicate, to work in a team, and to reflect on their own situation so that they can continuously improve their own performance. This comes about when talented people are encouraged to keep finding better answers.

However, the case studies show that often people need help and encouragement to move beyond their own professional or craft discipline. They also need training to develop core skills such as process analysis, work planning, problem solving, and performance measurement.

It is not easy for people who have learnt how to survive in the traditional industry to suddenly change. They often need training in cooperative behaviour. This can begin at workshops but needs to be reinforced by short courses and encouraged by consistent support from senior management. It has to be recognised that not everyone can develop adequate skills in cooperative behaviour. When this happens, the core team must either replace that individual or, in exceptional cases, decide to make special provisions for a person who is especially talented in some other respect. In either case, the core team must act when individuals work without taking other peoples' interests into account.

Because Partnering is tough, everyone should be selected very carefully to match the needs of the project. They have to be picked with the process in mind. They need to be confident about their own technical knowledge and experienced in the type of project planned. And the 'chemistry' needs to be right so project core teams form a balanced team. This means including people who between them provide the full range of characteristics required for effective team working. It is often worth using consultants or tests to ensure that all the team roles are provided by at least one of the people involved.

Individuals have the primary responsibility for developing their own skills, but firms experienced in Partnering encourage and reward those who make this effort as both benefit as a result.

MEMBERSHIP REVIEW

Performance should be measured regularly and firms that fall below a defined minimum should expect to lose the work if they do not improve quickly. Also there should be opportunities for new firms that can offer extra benefits to become preferred suppliers.

For all these reasons membership should be kept under review to ensure everyone plays a full role, is well motivated and continues to search for better ways of working.

Membership gem - Forming balanced teams

Several of the cases researched have employed consultants to build balanced teams. Those employed by Sainsbury's and Distribution Partnering both used Belbin tests to ensure core teams include people able to play all the following roles:

- **The Chairman** – the person who presides over the team and coordinates the work
- **The Shaper** – the task leader who drives the team to action
- **The Plant** – the source of original ideas
- **The Monitor-Evaluator** – the person who carefully dissects the ideas that the team is considering and sees the problems
- **The Resource-Investigator** – the popular member of the team who brings new contacts, ideas and developments into the team
- **The Company Worker** – the practical organiser who turns ideas into manageable tasks and then schedules and plans them
- **The Team Worker** – holds the team together by supporting others, by listening, encouraging and understanding
- **The Finisher** – checks the details, worries about schedules and chases others to ensure that the team meets its deadlines

Research shows that too many of one type in a team means a lack of balance; too few roles and some tasks never get done. In a small team one person may have to perform more than one role.

Membership gem - How Rover reviews membership and measures performance

Rover's Purchasing Department undertakes annual performance reviews of the three main contractors it has in its Partnering Team. It also reviews the other preferred suppliers, consultants and subcontractors. To do this Rover employs a supplier development tool called RG2000 that it uses throughout the whole of its business to encourage partnering and the continuous improvement it delivers.

RG2000 measures outputs and results on a scale of 0 (very poor) to 3 (very good). Contractors are scored on some 20 main criteria. For each there are procedures to define what is to be measured and provide detailed guidance for calculating the appropriate score. Any features of a contractor's performance scoring either 0 to 1 must be improved. The search for improvement begins by auditing the processes that contribute to the weak performance. This forces firms to understand their own work and why it delivers the performances that it does.

The Purchasing Department has four facilitators working with the building industry firms that Rover uses. They evaluate the main contractors and about 100 key suppliers and subcontractors. An important part of this annual performance review is to establish the level of overheads and profits that will be charged by the firms for the next 12 months. This is always expected to be, and is, lower that the year before because of improved performance.

In order to help the preferred firms adopt the Partnering approach Rover have invested in training for two core skills which are central to Partnering. These are cooperative teamworking and cost control based on an open book approach.

The fundamental issue dealt with by the equity pillar is that traditional building work is funded project by project, whereas Second Generation Partnering requires firms to invest long-term.

LONG-TERM DEVELOPMENT

There are several examples of clients with regular building programmes funding long-term development work. The bigger contracting and some consultancy firms are also now undertaking some long-term R&D. Specialists and manufacturers are also well suited to being involved in ongoing strategic development as they include many large firms with the financial strength to act long-term.

The case studies include several examples where Partnering teams have formally agreed to contribute to the cost of development work independently of any specific project. The usual arrangements are for each member to agree to fund a proportion of the costs.

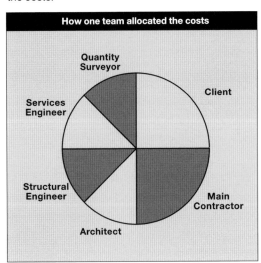

How one team allocated the costs

- Quantity Surveyor
- Client
- Services Engineer
- Main Contractor
- Structural Engineer
- Architect

GOVERNMENT FUNDING

Firms can look beyond their own resources for the finance for long-term development work. Most importantly, Government R&D funding through DTI, DETR and the Research Councils has been instrumental in setting up a number of successful joint initiatives. These normally include links between industry and universities or other research bodies. Indeed much of the work of Reading Construction Forum uses partnering arrangements between industry and research.

PRIVATE SECTOR FUNDING

Most firms will ultimately rely on shareholders or customers to provide the resources they need.

One possible source of shareholder funding, at least for the bigger building companies, is overseas construction companies seeking a presence in the UK. A number have already acquired stakes in UK businesses and have brought with them a greater willingness to think and invest for the future.

The other primary source of finance is the industry's clients. There are two promising ways in which

clients may provide more long-term development finance.

SAVINGS FROM PARTNERING

The savings delivered from Partnering can either be used to improve profit margins or used to invest in improved long-term solutions. Some leading clients appear to want to take the lion's share of the rewards. This may make short-term commercial sense but provides no basis for the industry to invest long-term. Building firms will have to overcome these traditional short-term attitudes if they are to get the full rewards that partnering can provide. Achieving this is an important role of the equity pillar.

PRIVATE FINANCE INITIATIVE

PFI schemes are transforming the way firms think about their work in a way that fits exactly with the needs of Partnering. The PFI requires firms to think long-term. Whole life operational costs have to be taken into account and quality and maintainability have to be considered in new ways. Even more fundamentally designers and financiers have to understand how buildings are used and are likely to be used in the future.

PFI schemes invariably include several firms providing distinctive skills and resources. Some are led by major contractors but there are many other firms involved including investment banks, management consultants, manufacturers, IT companies, and various types of service and facilities management companies. PFI projects encourage firms to work together and think long-term and they should create the potential for development work to be funded from part of the income stream the project's generate.

MAINTAINING COMMITMENT TO DEVELOPMENT WORK

Having found the money, it is also important to organise the development work so that the firms involved remain committed to continuing to support it. Key ways of maintaining commitment involve:

- rotation of staff between the development team and mainstream practice, usually on a three year cycle
- setting clearly defined objectives that are broad enough to encourage creativity and innovation but tightly defined enough to avoid the development group drifting into open ended research
- ensuring close links to live projects so that research teams can help project teams solve difficult challenges
- establishing a multi-discipline development team with the time and resources to find new answers
- ensuring close links to research institutes so development teams know what is happening at the leading edge of their fields of knowledge
- systematic use of tests and prototypes to ensure that new ideas are practical and effective before they are handed over

- joint work between development and project teams when new ideas are introduced into mainstream practice
- ensuring well organised feedback from live projects

TYPICAL AREAS FOR DEVELOPMENT WORK

The lessons from the case studies suggest that good subjects for long-term development work are:

- understanding users' needs over the lifetime of the facility
- providing flexibility to ensure a facility remains useful over its lifetime
- managing the risks involved in financing, producing and running a facility
- devising performance measures that concentrate attention on areas where costs can be driven down without sacrificing quality

OWNERSHIP OF INNOVATIONS

Agreeing the ownership of a new innovative solution is often the earliest major hurdle in the partnering process and the outcome of such negotiations can set the tone for the ongoing relationship.

The ownership issue is complicated, particularly when an unanticipated solution occurs or when an innovation emerges from an unexpected source. Trying to negotiate ownership afterwards often leads to conflict. Therefore addressing this issue early and formalising the expectations of all partners is a prudent step. The best solution is to allow new technologies to flow to the partner with the strongest strategic match with the new market. In other words new ideas are owned jointly and all the partners have the right to develop them further either inside or outside the partnering arrangement. The market then determines where the benefits accrue. So this

Equity gem - Ownership of innovations

Chetwood Associates is a firm of architects that has grown rapidly by focusing on building long-term relationships with clients in specific market sectors. In particular, the firm has become well regarded in the distribution marketplace, mainly via its partnering relationship with Distribution Partnering. The firm has built a body of information from previous projects into libraries of standard details that can be accessed by its different offices via the firm's intranet. This has significantly sharpened and speeded up the processing of information. The firm has a library of standard details for distribution facilities that also includes specifications, details of any problems that have arisen and how these problems were resolved. This information helps Chetwood produce drawings quicker and avoids repeating errors. The common set of details are jointly owned in respect of Distribution Partnering's projects, but Chetwood use them freely for its other clients.

approach gives all the firms involved the right to use the jointly developed version of a new technology in any way they choose as long as they do not undermine its joint ownership.

SHARING THE BENEFITS FAIRLY

One of the main challenges to long-term development that emerged from the case studies was that some parties felt that a disproportionate share of the benefits accrued to other people. In these instances, a review of the strategic business plan can remove the doubts. If the benefits are being unfairly shared out the case for a redistribution needs to be agreed. If it is simply a perception problem then training can be the answer.

Equity gem - How Arlington established a fair price, improved quality and avoided claims

On Arlington's business park at Theale near Reading the contractors were heavily involved in 'learning' about each new office building, before agreeing a fixed price.

Arlington began the procurement process by appointing an independent design team to validate and respond to its initial brief. The team was then asked to produce a concept design and progress this to scheme design stage. Arlington's budget for the project was based on market considerations.

Although the design was well developed the professional team was asked not to specify products or systems – for example the cladding – so that the contractors had lee-way to exercise their commercial and technical skills.

Once the design team was happy with the scheme design three potential contractors were asked to participate in the first stage of the tender process and to provide a set of competitive rates based on their developed understanding of the scheme.

When the selected contractor was appointed he spent four months working with the project team so he could absorb Arlington's culture and approach, and fully understand the design that was proposed. He was also encouraged to undertake site investigations and any other studies he need so he could fully evaluate any potential risks. By working closely with Arlington's professional team to further refine the scheme he was able to agree how risks were managed. By the time the second stage tender was submitted the contractor was happy to take full responsibility for all design work and delivered the building for an agreed fixed price.

Arlington got the building to the agreed quality standard, at exactly the agreed price (without risk of claims), and had a single-point warranty.

It is necessary for people involved in Partnering to recognise that while it is legitimate for them to do as well as their counterparts they should not compare themselves with others who are doing different work. Thus a developer is likely to make bigger profits from any given volume of work than, say, an architect. What matters is that the architect is doing at least as well as any other architect would do in the context of the partnering arrangement. Such concerns should, however, be expressed, fully debated and resolved at workshops.

The issue of ownership becomes more complicated as Partnering involves suppliers throughout the various supply chains. Each firm will need to know what is involved in the arrangement for them in terms of profit, bottom line value, turnover, payment terms, continuity and other benefits, including the ownership of jointly developed new technologies.

As the Partnering arrangement spreads through the supply chains, it is important that there are clear and fair arrangements in place to deal with all these issues.

LOOKING AFTER KEY PEOPLE

Another important challenge concerns the career prospects for staff involved in long-term Partnering developments. Incentives need to be considered for individuals because getting involved in developing cooperative partnering skills involves considerable personal investment and risk. Firms engaged in Partnering should ensure their staff understand the benefits. Individuals involved in partnering become more efficient in their own work through having to debate and justify decisions within a team. The case studies show that experienced and talented people who have built their careers in the traditionally adversarial culture prevalent in construction often need time and support from their senior managers before they are able to make these changes.

PROJECT INCENTIVES AND COSTS

The benefits delivered from Partnering provide scope for incentives. In agreeing how rewards are to be dealt with the goal should be to align everyone's interests with fully meeting the client's objectives. This means arranging the payments to each firm so that their profits increase directly with the success of the project. The way rewards are handled should ensure everyone involved can concentrate on achieving agreed mutual objectives without having to worry about whether they will get paid for what they do. This is tremendously energising and very efficient. The worst situations arise when some of the firms involved are losing money.

Therefore, providing a fair return for everyone involved should be an important aim.

It is difficult to establish effective incentives for a group of firms with little or no experience of Partnering as many of the building industry's normal practices cause people to concentrate on financial issues and so make it difficult for them to work effectively. For these reasons it is often best to begin

the move to Partnering using a simple agreement to share any savings identified by teams on some pre-determined basis.

There are costs involved in Partnering and these need to be taken into account in agreeing how the rewards are to be dealt with. Specific costs include training in cooperative ways of working and such things as the development and use of flexible cost control systems that encourage creativity and new ideas. Also Partnering requires regular workshops that bring the team together to build or reinforce cooperative ways of working. These are most effective when they are held in purpose designed conference facilities and employ an independent facilitator. The project team need to agree how they are to be paid for – in best practice they are seen simply as part of the overall project budget.

REALISTIC COSTS AND PRICES

Throughout the process it is important for the client to be realistic about the budget and for consultants and contractors to be realistic about their prices. This means everyone agreeing only to costs and prices that they know they have a good chance of sticking to.

OPEN BOOK ACCOUNTS

The use of fair open book arrangements, guided by tough cost control and audits is now commonplace in best practice partnering. The case studies show that this provides a basis for firms to totally alter the way they work. Instead of defending their own narrow interests in an adversarial manner, a fair approach to the financial arrangements causes them to think and act as a team. They accept that there is a fixed amount of money available and their responsibility is to provide the best possible value.

Currently best practice is for the client to pay the firms it is Partnering with an agreed sum which provides a fair profit and contribution to their fixed overheads plus all their properly incurred direct costs. This makes it much easier for people to concentrate on doing whatever is in the best interests of the project to eliminate unproductive activities. When they know they will be paid for whatever they do as long as they are honestly seeking to add value for the client, people are prepared to try new ideas, join in task forces and experiment with prototypes to find the best answers. Working in this way requires open book accounting, well-developed cost control and tough auditing. Setting up these systems takes time and requires firms that are experienced in Partnering.

BENCHMARKS

Whichever approach is adopted, project teams need some means of assuring the client that the agreed price provides value for money. Benchmarking projects for the same client is the most effective approach, but where this is not possible, using benchmarks from similar projects for other clients provides an effective alternative to competitive tendering.

In order for partnering firms to be really effective they need to integrate their systems so completely that they form an efficient 'virtual organisation'. A good test of progress is that in properly formed Partnering organisations everyone behaves in a consistent manner when you deal with them.

TRUST

"I believe that if someone trusts me, then that places a greater onus and responsibility on me than any contract ever written."
Brian Fox, SDC Builders, quoted in Building 5 August 1994

Without trust teams lack the basis for open, mutual learning, communication and real integration. Trust allows teams to focus on interests rather than on personalities or positions. Trust promotes openness and encourages people to put their cards on the table. A sign of trust between two parties is that they are both committed to try to understand each other's point of view and work together for the 'Third Alternative' – the synergistic solution that provides a better answer for all parties involved.

In order to develop trust, you have to show genuine respect and appreciation for the other person and their point of view. Trust and respect are linked. They enable people to communicate better. When you feel that another person respects your views, you stay longer in the communication process, you listen in greater depth, you express yourself with greater courage and you are not reactive.

In developing trust secrecy is always damaging. Talking openly nearly always provides two-way benefits.

CONTINUITY

In building up integration it is important to remove cynicism about how the relationship is going to develop and to be totally open and positive right from the start. Integration takes time to develop and so it is helped by continuity. Effective Strategic Teams take every opportunity to allow people to work together long-term so they learn to trust each other and develop cooperative ways of working. Real integration depends on knowing, understanding and even establishing the rules of the game.

LEVELS OF INTEGRATION

The case studies show that the depth of integration required for Partnering to deliver its full benefits involves internal as well as external changes. Both take time and need sustained commitment. This means that in practice the internal and external changes have to be pursued in parallel. Supply chain management is the key technique used to achieve integration.

Five levels of integration have been identified to enable firms to achieve the most productive relationships:

STRATEGIC INTEGRATION

This exists between top management who decide goals and objectives and identify changes that are necessary. The more information communicated at this level and the more contact top managers in the separate firms have, the greater the possibility that the companies will evolve in cooperative rather than conflicting directions. In construction, strategic integration often begins with principals' meetings that address big challenges and provide leadership in ensuring continual progress in integrating the other four levels.

TACTICAL INTEGRATION

Effective teamworking at this level brings together middle managers and professionals operating at equivalent levels of responsibility. Their role is to develop plans for specific projects or joint activities, to identify organisational or system changes and transfers of information that will link the companies better.

As an example, Sainsbury's measure store managers' reactions to its buildings to improve its understanding of what is important and what is causing difficulties. One outcome was that snagging was identified as a problem, so it appointed a Snagging Manager with a wide remit to work with its partnering consultants and contractors to change their joint systems so as to eliminate snagging within three years.

OPERATIONAL INTEGRATION

This level of integration provides ways for people carrying out day-to-day work to have timely access to the information, resources or people they need to accomplish their tasks. The aim should be to build up an attitude of 'whoever sees a problem owns it." This means that when problems are spotted they are not ignored. If people are competent to deal with it, they do so; if it is outside their competence, they make sure that someone who is competent deals with it. Getting first-level managers to accept this is critical to Partnering.

INTERPERSONAL INTEGRATION

Many people need to know those in other organisations personally, before they will make the effort to exchange technology, provide access to clients or participate in joint teams. Good interpersonal relationships also help resolve small conflicts before they escalate.

CULTURAL INTEGRATION

Cultures have to be matched. This level requires people to have the communication skills and cultural awareness to express themselves in other people's terms. In effect managers have to accept the need for learning based on mutual interest and respect. This helps to bridge cultural and organisational differences.

BUILDING COOPERATION

Building integration requires that individuals have a sufficiently large chance of working together again that they have a stake in ensuring success. The expectation of future work is essential to ensure cooperation. Where people do not expect to work together again, they tend to act selfishly and seek their own narrow advantage.

In the past there was a cultural problem ingrained in the industry's normal methods of working whereby it was politically correct to rely on short-termism and individual contractual relationships. Successful firms were described as having a competitive advantage, and Governments actively encouraged competition.

The case for cooperation is now increasingly powerful. This is encouraging for building industry firms attempting to Partner as they will increasingly find that clients and other firms are receptive to acting cooperatively.

The research undertaken to support this report shows that when leading clients select firms, they are beginning to look at a contractor's track record of working cooperatively with other clients. As a result, firms not willing to cooperate will find this affects their reputation adversely. Contractors who have a reputation for non-cooperation are increasingly losing contracts with leading clients.

INTERNAL CONFLICT

A common barrier to successful partnering is internal conflict within the individual firms. There may be a lack of trust, power struggles or internal policies that prevent some people from being effective team players.

It is not uncommon for organisations with internal problems to look externally for the source of their problems and fail to recognise that a major cause of their difficulties is on their own doorstep. The change to a partnering culture is a big step for many organisations and individuals. The first move often needs to be internal partnering

INTERNAL PARTNERING

A consistently cooperative approach is essential for Partnering to succeed. This could begin with an internal evaluation of the changes needed for Partnering to succeed. By making the whole of the organisation aware of the ideas of Partnering, people are more likely to join in searching for more effective ways of working. Partnering Champions find they

Integration gem - How Showcase Cinemas encourage specialist contractors to co-operate

Showcase Cinemas has a long standing partnering relationship with ZVI Construction (UK) – the European arm of a Boston based construction management company and with the key specialist contractors. The Managing Director of ZVI is directly involved in the execution of the works and is a major motivating influence with the rest of the team. Strong leadership also comes from the Project Managers of the main specialist trade contractors, each of whom is expected to become more dominant in leading other trades when their particular activity is on the critical path. Frequent meetings are called to address resource planning, shared use of plant/facilities in congested areas, overcoming any unforeseen design problems and to exchange views on performance and quality. While these meetings are generally cordial a frank exchange of views is the norm particularly if the performance of one trade contractor is perceived by another to be below par. A problem experienced by one team member is now seen as concern to them all. This one-team philosophy has extended to unloading and distributing each other's materials and the shared use of plant. The adoption of a cooperative approach by the trade contractors is one of the most positive benefits of the partnering approach.

have to overcome fear and resistance to change from often powerful people, including finance, administration, purchasing, etc. The essential internal preparation usually needs to take place in parallel with developing external Partnering.

JOINT IT STRATEGIES

A good early initiative for Partnering firms is to develop a joint IT strategy. Partnering requires a high level of communication and this is often assisted by establishing integrated IT networks. Doing this also serves to highlight potential internal problems. The case studies show that while there is an initial cost in setting up integrated networks, the long-term benefits far outweigh the investment.

IT integration often begins with the use of electronic mail and compatible computer packages, so that information can be transported more efficiently. The case studies also include firms using video conferencing to reduce the time and costs of travel for senior managers.

The effort involved in setting up IT systems naturally leads to a deeper analysis of the joint processes served by the network. A key responsibility of

Strategic Teams is to keep analysing their joint processes so as to maintain continuous improvement.

INTEGRATED BEHAVIOURS

To achieve integration means working at developing attitudes, behaviours and structures. This means that Partnering Champions need to work at four levels in developing trust and cooperation.

- Accept the evidence that trust and cooperation work better than suspicion and adversarial tactics. Accept that ultimately the only way to build trust is to ensure agreements which work as planned every time. After dishonesty the failure to deliver what was promised is the biggest source of organisational mistrust.

- Reward people for taking risks to build trust and cooperation internally within the company. Make buyers and sellers feel good when they are open about their own organisation's needs in dealing with organisations that are important to their firm. Encourage your top team to display confidence in their own people's judgement, and educate them in the principles of relationship management. Ensure that everyone involved in managing partnering arrangements gets feedback from their bosses, peers and subordinates on how they are perceived to behave in respect to trust and cooperation.

- Provide internal and external structures that facilitate trust and cooperation and provide plenty of opportunity for communication and feedback – both ways. Never use feedback as a basis for blame or punishment. Its purpose is continuous improvement and so it must always be treated positively.

- Invest time and money in openly supporting the aspirations of the people you are Partnering with. Take risks on areas of common ground or joint interests. Do not expect people to take risks for your company if they cannot see some clear pay-off for themselves. Trust and cooperation cannot be one-way streets. For example it is important that main contractors do not crush their smaller suppliers under bureaucracy or unreasonable demands. People will not be effective in Partnering arrangements if they ignore the interests of smaller firms.

COMPETENCE

It has to be remembered that Partnering depends on competence. There is no point in even attempting to Partner with incompetent people. Partnering needs tough, competent people at all levels. Trust and cooperation therefore depends on the membership pillar being given careful attention.

BENEFITS

Given competent people, well developed integration gives them the freedom to do their best work. Practical benefits include fewer inspections and audits, fewer decision levels and faster communications. The most important benefit is that it makes it easier to trust others and adopt cooperative behaviour which then produces genuine win:win situations.

Integration gem - How the Heathrow Express team goes about building trust

The Heathrow Express team set itself the challenge of agreeing a Partnering Charter which would define the standards by which its members wished to be judged.

It agreed the following five key elements in the Charter:-

T for **Teamwork** – all organisations would work together

R for **Resource** – management would commit to provide the Team with sufficient resources

U for **Understanding** – mutual understanding of each others position was critical

S for **Support** – everyone supports each other; from the top to the front line teams

T for **Truth** – openness and honesty would prevail at all times

The result was **TRUST**.

Three factors underpinned this trust. Firstly, demonstrable and patent trust between the senior managers. Secondly, sharing budgets so that no-one could win at anyone else's expense and thirdly, shared celebrations – if the project scored a goal, everyone was part of the success and shared in the celebrations.

**The key aim of Second Generation Partnering
is to deliver continuous improvements over a
series of projects. This pillar deals with the
need to measure these continuous
improvements in ways that encourage people
to search for innovation.**

ASSURANCE FOR CLIENTS

The measurements used should be capable of
comparing cost, time, quality, service, etc. with that
being achieved by other firms in the same market
sector i.e. they should provide benchmarks. In this
way clients can be assured that they are getting good
value for their money.

PRACTICAL BENCHMARKS

Benchmarks help prevent long-term relationships
becoming cosy or sloppy by providing objective
measures of the ongoing achievements.

Benchmarks should be simple, robust, widely
understood and measure what is important to the
client's business. Measurements have to be
believable so people can relate to them. In particular
they need to demonstrate cost competitiveness.
Good examples include:

- total cost per square metre
- square metres of building constructed per day
  on site
- total time from inception to occupancy
- number of defects at handover
- complaints from users about their building
- customers' views about the building
- life-cycle-costs

QUICK WINS

It is important with a new Partnering arrangement to
choose measures for the first projects which will
show significant benefits quickly. A good approach
is to produce at a Partnering Workshop a list of all the
issues that any of the parties regard as important.
Each item on the list should be discussed and then
each of the people present at the Partnering
Workshop should be asked to nominate the most
important measure. By this means a small number of
really significant measures should be identified.
Each should be discussed in detail to decide exactly
how the measurements will be produced.

ROBUST MEASUREMENTS

Interesting approaches that may help in the search
for robust measures include:

- Measuring how long it takes to halve the time of
  individual processes.
- Measuring how long it takes to halve the number
  of defects.
- Asking the customer how effective the Partnering
  team is at listening to their concerns and needs
  and how effective the team is at responding to
  what it hears.

- Discussing what 'winning' means in the context
  of the Partnering arrangement and then
  developing measures to satisfy this criteria. In
  these discussions it is important to remember
  that measures should accurately reflect the
  client's objectives so as to concentrate
  everyone's attention on the important issues.

In deciding the benchmarks to be used it is important
to remember that the way performance is measured
influences the way workers behave – they attend to
the things that are measured and are inclined to
neglect the rest.

WHAT TO BENCHMARK

In deciding what to benchmark, at least three
separate subjects should be considered. These
relate to the performance of:

- the overall partnering arrangement
- individual projects
- individual firms

In deciding on the benchmarks used it is important
that they are consistent with a common-sense,
practical view of success. Benchmarks would be
quickly discredited if they suggested that the
strategic arrangement was doing well, while several
of the partnering firms were losing money and users
were not happy with their new buildings.

ROUTINE BENCHMARKS

A key responsibility for the Strategic Team is to agree
how improvements in joint performance are to be
measured. A good place to start is with the
measurements that are already routinely produced
within the individual firms as part of their
management control systems. The Strategic Team
should review these to identify what is important and
what can be measured accurately and efficiently.

Benchmarks are needed that can show convincingly
that Partnering involves less risks and delivers bigger
rewards. They should take account of the need to
identify and measure continuous improvements.

OBJECTIVE AND SUBJECTIVE BENCHMARKS

It is helpful to consider both objective and subjective
measures. The judgement of experienced
professionals, especially where several people make
independent judgements and then debate them, is
an entirely valid basis for measuring the performance
of project teams. This is especially so where
subjective judgements are combined with well
defined objective measurements to provide a broad
evaluation. All of these issues need to be considered
by the Strategic Team. Out of the ensuing
discussions they should identify about four
measurements that reflect the improvements they
want to make in their joint performance.

BENCHMARKS FOR PROJECTS AND FIRMS

The performance of both projects and firms should be measured.

Project benchmarks should derive directly from the measured benefits used in the management of individual projects. They should deal with the objectives set at the strategic level so that the Strategic Team can make consistent comparisons of the performance of individual projects. Measurement is an integral element in the management of projects and so should form part of normal work. It should not need extra resources nor should it be expensive.

Benchmarks for individual firms are usually based on aggregating measurements produced on the projects that they are involved in over a given time period plus further specific measures of, for example, their level of investment in new equipment, training, etc.

INVOLVING THE WORKERS

In agreeing targets it is good practice to involve people in setting their own goals. There is strong evidence to show that when workers are given the responsibility for setting their own targets and supplied with objective benchmarks of what other people in similar situations are achieving, they will set very tough targets for themselves. The research suggests that Partnering works best when there is somebody leading the arrangement, frequently the client, who constantly encourages project core teams to set tough targets.

REGULAR BENCHMARKS

Once agreed the benchmarks should be measured at regular intervals so the rate of improvement is evident. Control charts that record performance over time are one important part of preventing Partnering relationships becoming inefficient. They should be produced regularly and the trends discussed by the Strategic Team as part of its ongoing search for continuous improvement.

OVERCOMING RESISTANCE

It is often necessary – even when good improvements are identified – to overcome well rehearsed resistance to change. In one of the case studies where Partnering was in its early stages a specialist contractor proposed using standardised fabric reinforcement mats instead of individual bars to simplify the construction processes, improve productivity, speed up the work and make its completion on time more certain. The improvement was well thought out in terms of his own work and costs but was resisted by the main contractor because the use of a complicated individual design often gives rise to claims which can boost his profit margins. The change was also opposed by the structural engineer because it meant less design work and therefore lower fees.

MANAGING CHANGE

The rate of change in markets and technologies has now become so rapid that organisations have to make change after change in order to stay ahead of their competitors. However, alongside this managers still need to search for areas of certainty that allow efficient processes to develop. It is in these areas that Partnering will be most effective.

Benchmarks gem - How Asda used Benchmarking to tackle dust control on its sites

Asda has five preferred main contractors for its stores – GA Construction, Kyle Stewart, Laing, Pearce and Tarmac Building. Their aim is to improve the service they provide to Asda by working together. They all recognise their performance will improve more if they work in concert than if they simply tackle problems individually. The first benchmarking study involved a study of dust control on renewal projects. This was seen as a non-competitive issue but it had given rise to complaints from Asda's store managers. The work was planned at a series of four workshops attended by a representative from each contractor and an independent facilitator.

The following actions were identified to search for better approaches to dust management:

- Devise, test and refine practical measures of the problem.
- Agree a procedure for using the measures to collect reliable data.
- Use the agreed procedure to determine whether there really is a problem and if so, its extent.
- Produce a map of the processes that influence the problem.
- Use the process map to identify the causes of the problem.
- Brainstorm possible solutions.
- Consult specialist contractors about causes and solutions.
- Obtain specialist advice on promising solutions.
- Try the most promising solutions and measure the effects.
- Draft and test instructions for site staff that turn the most promising solutions into practical actions and incorporate them into a best practice manual.
- Organise training for site managers in the new procedures.
- Purchase any specialised equipment needed.
- Put the agreed answers into effect and measure the results regularly.
- Ensure that Asda is aware of the improvement in performance.

In addition to solving the dust problem, the five contractors have learnt to work together cooperatively.

STRATEGIC TASK FORCES

An important contribution to making improvements is setting up well resourced strategic task forces made up of staff drawn from across the partnering firms. Each task force should have a clear objective and timetable aimed at achieving a specific improvement. Common subjects for strategic task forces include establishing joint communication systems, the development of new markets or finding new technical innovations.

BENCHMARKING

Benchmarks often lead into full blown Benchmarking. This is a very structured search for continuous improvement. Benchmarking provides a way of identifying weaknesses in current working methods and then searching for improvements by analysing similar processes. Interesting examples of Benchmarking include a group of five contractors who are all Partnering with the same client. They have recognised that they are in competition, not with each other, but with all the other contractors who currently do not work for the client. By Benchmarking their different approaches to common processes they hope to so improve the service they provide that the client that he will never look outside the five of them.

STEP CHANGES

Firms involved in Second Generation Partnering often look for new opportunities with their partners and invest in exploring potential new businesses as a matter of routine. They also encourage their staff to work together to search for new products, radically better ways of working, and more effective marketing. The search for these kinds of step changes to their joint businesses are pursued in parallel to working at continuously improving their ongoing business.

The search for step changes can be organised in different ways within Second Generation Partnering. Cases exist where a separate organisation is formed to undertake R&D. This may be structured as a joint venture or simply a long-term task force set up by the Partnering Team.

SKUNK GROUPS

Innovation often emerges from activities at or outside the boundaries of the formal organisations involved. The teams involved in such work are sometimes called skunk groups because they develop ideas to which they are personally highly committed, but to which their firms are unwilling to allocate resources. So they 'cheat' by using time, materials and equipment without the authority to produce something new. Studies of firms that have stayed in business for a very long time show that one thing they have in common is tolerance of skunk groups. They know that the high commitment generated from allowing people to work on things that really interests them benefits all their work. More importantly experience has taught them that when they face radical change which threatens their mainstream business, the firm's salvation often comes from one of their skunk groups having developed a new way forward. Best practice Partnering reflects this experience by encouraging people to explore new ideas and potential opportunities.

Benchmarks gem - How Whitbread monitors user's views on construction performance

Whitbread seeks feedback on construction performance in a number of ways. For example it measures how quickly its contractors respond, how long they take to correct defects and its customers' views on designs. The operating staff of its various pubs, restaurants and hotels also complete a satisfaction rating. Without this sort of positive feedback the whole essence of Partnering would be lost.

Whitbread's term maintenance and refurbishment contractors have an annual Maintenance Contractors Conference. The company's partners for new build work also attend this event and have consequently established relationships with the maintenance contractors in their areas. Information on repairs assists project teams in making value judgements about design issues.

The traditional processes in the UK building industry are sequential and consequently slow. They allow the traditional professions to work independently to produce individual designs. In support of traditional processes, architects, builders, engineers and surveyors have developed an impressive range of procedures to help coordinate their work. The scheme of Coordinated Project Information recommended by the Latham Report is an important example of these procedures, as is the JCT form of contract. When independent professionals stick to well established designs and technologies, their work fits together with little need for direct communication between them.

NEED FOR CHANGE

Today's clients want quality, speed and value for money. This puts the traditional approach under severe pressure as the separate processes need to merge, take place simultaneously or are simply inappropriate.

The principle aim of Partnering is to improve performance. When people keep working in the traditional way there are very real limits to the savings that can be achieved. Improved performance requires that processes are examined and then made more efficient. Process analysis, measurement and improvement are the keys to improved performance.

FUNDAMENTAL CHANGE

Second Generation Partnering tackles this head on and in doing so makes fundamental changes to the way individual projects are tackled. Projects are no longer just discrete sets of actions with a clear beginning and end – Second Generation Partnering turns projects into the 'components' of an ongoing long-term activity.

Project teams contribute to the much larger opportunity to deliver improvements provided by an ongoing series of projects. In return they have less discretion in how they tackle individual projects. This change alters the traditional work of all the building professions.

STANDARDS AND PROCEDURES

To give effect to this new way of working, individual projects are guided by processes that use standards and procedures developed by task forces or by feedback from projects. The standards and procedures provide many of the required design details and define predetermined roles, patterns for meetings, flows of information, and planning and control systems. In this way they can create an almost automatic way of working.

PRODUCTS AND PROCESSES

The strategic initiatives take different forms. Some focus on continuously improving the product – effectively standardising the building. Others focus on continuously improving the process by standardising design, manufacturing and/or construction processes. As a result there are a range of approaches that, viewed in total, provide suitable ways of applying systematic continuous improvement to many types of buildings.

STANDARD BUILDINGS

At one extreme end of the range is the standardised approach of McDonalds. By a direct use of manufacturing methods, McDonalds has developed and continuously improved a range of eight standard buildings that meet all its needs for stand alone fast food outlets. Once all the necessary approvals are available, the current version of the selected standard building can be produced very quickly, thus allowing the income stream from a new outlet to begin much earlier than with traditional methods. The buildings match the performance levels of traditional methods, yet are significantly cheaper to produce. Esso use substantially similar techniques for its service stations. Both companies have plans to use the approach on a world-wide scale and to therefore potentially provide ever better value for money.

STANDARDISED DESIGN PROCESSES

A different approach has been adopted by Waitrose which has developed three standardised design processes for its new supermarkets. The design processes are structured via computer systems that are subject to continuous improvement based on feedback from existing supermarkets and R&D. Once a new site is available and Waitrose has decided on the mix of goods it will sell, the most appropriate of the three design processes is selected. This is then applied straightforwardly without further development. This approach allows each project to be undertaken efficiently by concentrating on realising a predetermined design. Any good ideas that emerge during the project are used, not on that project, but are considered carefully, properly developed and added to the standardised design processes used in the future.

GENERIC DESIGNS

Similarly Whitbread developed generic designs for the various types of buildings it needs for its leisure business. Sainsbury's also has a standardised approach to the main elements of its supermarkets. Esso has standardised the design of its service stations so that the only important variables are the anticipated volume of business and the configuration of the site. As mentioned above this approach has recently been further developed with the production of manufactured service stations. Gazeley has a highly consistent approach to the design and construction of large distribution warehouses. The much vaunted approach adopted by Stanhope for Broadgate provided for continuous improvement from phase to phase within one large project. Stockley Park provided with the same advantage as each new building applied the lessons from earlier ones.

Whitbread has a consistent approach to design that is continuously developed from project to project, with the design being the starting point for the next new scheme. Each project is separately priced and Whitbread's contractor partner assumes joint responsibility for delivery to cost, time and quality from a very early stage – in some cases before the site is even acquired. Some partners have now become involved in the very earliest stages and are working with Whitbread's acquisition teams to identify potential new sites.

The resulting efficient processes are continuously improved through the work of task forces. Whitbread usually builds its Beefeater Restaurants and Travel Inns together under a single contract. The two buildings use different technologies – timber frame and steel frame – but both are sensible choices for the buildings considered in isolation. However this approach can result in some complications as the work undertaken by the key trades does not coincide as the buildings become weather tight at different times.

Whitbread's contractor, Pearce assembled a task force to devise a simple process. The task force included the operators, design consultants, specialist contractors and Pearce's own design and construction staff and its solution was to opt for a timber frame for both buildings.

The simplified process was adopted as a new standard and, within the first year of using it, construction costs were reduced by 20%.

A STEP CHANGE FOR THE INDUSTRY

The emergence of these approaches to continuous improvement is a major development for the building industry. At present it is entirely client led and, as yet, is scarcely recognised by most of the construction sector.

Second Generation Partnering is essential for the industry to play its full part in the step change. All the pillars need to be in place so that project core teams can be assembled and work through a predetermined process. The key choice is whether they can work through a standardised process or whether they need a flexible process that is defined stage by stage as the project processes.

REPETITION

In either case it helps to aim for repetition within the project – for example the Second Severn Crossing was designed so that it involved repeated patterns of work which led to dramatic improvements in productivity as the project team gained experience of the work. This kind of improvement should be aimed for from the outset as repetition generally leads to improvements.

DESIGNING THE ORGANISATION

Once the choice between a standardised or a flexible process is made, the rest of the project organisation needs to be designed to support the selected approach.

All Distribution Partnering's projects begin with a creative analysis of every aspect of the project. Construction Management techniques are used during this initial stage to provide the flexibility needed for creative decision making. Once there is a clear definition of the work, and the risks and the guaranteed maximum price, the project moves to a second stage. At this point work is planned in detail and carried out in a controlled manner. Design build is used for the plan and control stage to provide the single point responsibility preferred by funding institutions.

Many of the team's projects use what is substantially an existing design based on standard details that are not changed during the project so the process is largely pre-determined. This provides the certainty that allows the team to make one or two carefully chosen improvements.

This well developed way of working has been captured in a short, punchy and easily readable handbook that ensures that lessons from individual projects are applied consistently. The principle aim of the handbook is to guide everyone in applying the same approach and methods. The handbook is also the basis of the structure adopted for the one-day workshops used at the start of Distribution Partnering's projects to help instil the required attitudes and methods in everyone involved.

Project Processes gem - Rover sets fixed, but flexible milestones

Rover's Group Design and Engineering Centre (GDEC) provides a world class car design facility by exploiting methods developed in the Japanese car industry and brought to Rover through its link with Honda.

Rover's simultaneous engineering approach to design meant that the detailed programmes were constantly changing. Having fixed milestones that were defined flexibly allowed the changes to be absorbed.

Time control was achieved by a process of detailed planning and regular checks within a best guess overall programme that was kept to by extraordinary efforts. The earliest and latest dates for non-critical items provided valuable flexibility between the milestones which SDC, the contractor, managed carefully.

SDC issued the team with the key deadlines for design information. This process flagged up conflicts of priorities between SDC and the designers and as a result SDC was required to constantly chase Rover and the designers for information. When the project was approaching a milestone, the programme became the most important issue.

The approach was robust enough to enable the scheme to absorb substantial changes. For example, soon after BMW acquired Rover a £1.4m entrance and atrium and an extra storey were added to part of the building. Steelwork in the areas affected had already been erected. This meant a hole had to be left for the entrance and atrium, which were added later.

Another example was that the cladding the team originally planned to use did not match the agreed quality vision. This problem arose at an awkward time just as BMW was buying Rover. As a result it was difficult to get decisions taken by the client. The team dealt with this by putting up a rainscreen so it could take the cladding off the critical path. The new system improved the fire safety but created a substantial overspend which could have potentially affected the programme and the budget significantly. However the team worked together to modify the steelwork and absorb all the additional costs from savings achieved elsewhere.

Throughout this process, not one letter was exchanged between SDC and Rover. No extension of time was sought and the original occupancy date was maintained. It is remarkable that these substantial changes provoked no claims or contractual issues. The team simply did what was needed to make the modifications safe in the knowledge that it would be paid its full costs.

A flexible process suits projects where new answers are needed. It relies on programmes and budgets that are interpreted flexibly in the light of actual progress as milestones are reached. This can provide a reasonable level of assurance for a client that cost and time targets will be met, though doing so requires a tough approach to decision making. A common answer in such projects is to set up a project office that brings the core team together for all the significant stages. A tough cost control system is also needed, often based on open book accounting and rigorous audit procedures. The project will also need a clear time control system to focus the team's attention on each set of critical issues as it works through the project. Quality control has to be robust and in the hands of experienced professionals who understand the technologies being used. In best practice the core team is engaged in a relentless search for the best possible answers within a fixed budget and handover date. This means that in designing the process, time should be provided to review the plan and make improvements as the work progresses.

Whenever possible a standardised process should be used. In a fully developed form it will be supported by good information systems that enable fixed targets to be set with confidence. When a well developed process has been established it enables projects to be carried out with great efficiency and certainty. Decisions will largely be made at formal meetings. It is likely that the project will progress in accordance with a predetermined plan and budget using standards and guided by clear procedures. Achieving this level of certainty and control takes time and steady development over many projects.

CONTROLLED CHANGE

Whatever the needs of the project, Partnering means looking for improvements in a controlled way.

Changes to project processes are best introduced gradually, one or two at a time. If everything changes all at once, people become disoriented and demotivated. Change has to be built up steadily step by step. In deciding on the process to be used, core teams need to agree on the standards and procedures to be used; and the one or two new steps they will take on their project.

In accepting this controlled way of working they should be motivated by knowing that they are making a strategic contribution to improved performance as well as managing their own project.

The construction industry has many innovative ideas that get lost because there is little systematic feedback. Lessons should be captured so that they are applied on future projects. This is commonly called positive feedback.

Feedback is also vital in ensuring that problems and defects do not re-occur. In these ways feedback provides the control loop for the virtual organisations formed by firms undertaking Second Generation Partnering.

PROCESS IMPROVEMENT

For feedback to play its full role, firms involved in Partnering need to develop standards and procedures that systematically capture best practice as it emerges from projects, strategic level workshops or task forces. It is especially important to focus on understanding and improving joint processes because this is where Second Generation Partnering provides its biggest benefits. A great deal of time and effort is wasted in negotiating and arguing over how interfaces are to be handled in traditional one-off situations. By using feedback to develop efficient standards and procedures, most of these actions become unnecessary, thus allowing project teams to concentrate on productive work.

PRACTICAL FEEDBACK

Feedback is used in this way to improve efficiency in many different situations. Indeed the efficiency of all controlled systems is improved by accurate and relevant feedback. In the UK building industry there is a widespread misconception that all projects are unique, so there is limited use of feedback. This view means mistakes are repeated, good ideas are lost and the industry's overall performance falls further behind other modern industries.

The building industry has developed some useful information systems that are driven by feedback. But unfortunately they rarely provide a central driving force for improvement. They include:-

- RICS's Building Cost Information Service
- BRE's Defects Database
- Published libraries of design details

STRATEGIC FOCUS

Second Generation Partnering provides a unique basis for feedback to play its proper role in improving performance. This operates at two levels. First, the Strategic Team should ensure that the processes worked to by individual project teams use systematic feedback to control their performance. To achieve this Partnering firms should invest jointly in developing robust feedback systems that can be used on the individual projects and then they should train all their staff in their use.

Second, Strategic Teams should make careful decisions about the feedback systems they use to guide their own work and that of strategic task forces towards meeting agreed strategic objectives. Thus if zero defects is a strategic objective, feedback on defects and their causes will be needed from each project. If fast construction is a strategic objective, feedback on deviations from planned progress will be helpful.

Ensuring that feedback systems are in place and working effectively in all the separate firms is often a task for the Partnering Champion.

APPLYING FEEDBACK

The Strategic Team needs to provide sufficient resources to ensure that relevant feedback from the individual projects is collected and analysed scientifically. The results should be discussed regularly by the Strategic Team and its conclusions should be fed into the standards and procedures that project teams use so that improvement is automatically built into normal working methods. Also the specific objectives set for individual projects should be guided by the strategic feedback so the targets are achievable, yet challenging.

DESIGNING FEEDBACK SYSTEMS

Deciding the specific feedback data to be collected and how it is to be used is a task for the Strategic Team. The basic elements of any feedback system are that a clear target is set, progress towards the target is measured and exceptions are identified. This is implicitly understood in the many cost and time control systems used throughout the building industry. There is great merit in making this explicit and being tough about applying the disciplines needed for feedback driven control systems to become virtually automatic.

The Strategic Team need to decide what aspects of individual projects should be subject to formal feedback systems. Cost and time are not always the most important aspects. In many situations it is more sensible to treat quality and safety with greater rigour. Indeed the great success of Japanese management methods is based on first controlling quality and then working to programme in a controlled manner. When quality and time are tightly controlled, efficiency is inherent in the work and so narrow cost control is less important. These issues should be debated by the Strategic Team in deciding on the feedback systems to set up.

FEEDBACK GUIDES DEVELOPMENT

The Strategic Team should also consider how

feedback can be used to guide new developments in working methods. These may include developing the use of standards that gradually change the nature of the work required on individual projects. For example, the use of prefabrication often begins experimentally in a series of trial approaches that are evaluated with the help of feedback. Improvements to processes also often depend on feedback. For example, improvements to the briefing process could link briefs to user feedback. Or improvements to cost estimating could link initial estimates to final accounts. Significant gaps between any planned and actual performance should trigger a review of the processes involved.

COMMUNICATING FEEDBACK

An issue that warrants careful thought by the Strategic Team is to decide who receives feedback, in what form and what they are authorised to do with the results. In designing such systems it is vital to consult the people involved about the form in which they need the feedback results. Some managers are happy to have no more than a list of exceptions to the plan. Others want to see the trends, while some

will be more comfortable if they can see the detailed data.

VIRTUALLY AUTOMATIC CONTROL

It is important that feedback systems should move towards providing virtually automatic control for projects undertaken within Strategic Partnering. This is becoming a matter of routine through the use of IT in the management processes in many sectors of the economy. Construction still has a lot of ground to make up to match best practice. Strategic Partnering provides the ideal environment to do just this.

PROJECT SUCCESS

The criteria for measuring project team success usually includes benchmarks on productivity (cost, schedule and profitability) and process (issues concerning safety, how well the team worked together, resolved issues and made organisational improvements).

WALK THE JOB

Even when good feedback systems are in place it is important that managers do not forget the importance of direct, personal knowledge. They should 'walk the job' in the offices, factories and construction sites wherever work is taking place on their project. They should ask questions of the people doing the work:

- What are your targets?
- How are you doing against your targets?
- How well did you do last week?
- What is the next milestone you have to meet?
- What quality standards do you work to?
- Do you know who your boss is?

CONTINUOUS IMPROVEMENT

This direct information combined with rigorous feedback data provides the safest basis for

Feedback gem - A Showcase for design feedback

Showcase Cinemas believes standard details are important in providing a focus for feedback. Although most cinema complexes contain many standardised elements each project is still subject to unique considerations. These variables are generally dictated by the number of screens to be installed, local planning constraints and ground conditions.

By utilising standardised detailing and structural methodology Showcase has been able to speed up construction. For example the original programme for its Coatbridge project east of Glasgow was bettered by two weeks and by the time the Beckton Project in East London had run its course a further week had been saved from the overall programme. Both these early completions resulted in improved revenues for Showcase.

Showcase now welcomes suggestions from its design teams on how it can improve or speed up the detailed design. This feedback is encouraged and regarded as positive. More importantly, the ideas are often adopted as a standard detail for future projects. The value of the feedback process is well illustrated by the fact that originally the cinema's external walls consisted of a complex mix of technologies and trades including a non-load bearing masonry outerface, structural steelwork and insulated internal studwork which formed acoustic walls. Using value engineering techniques, costs were reduced dramatically by using a single structural element that provides the structural support, fire barrier and acoustic control.

This approach also sped up the process and meant that internal dividing walls could be constructed before the roof was completed.

Feedback gem - Esso uses Feedback to drive its improvements in cost and design

Esso's systematic development of a standard shop consciously set out to encourage feedback from each of its local businesses across Europe.

The result was therefore a pan-European 'standard' plus a range of optional extras. In establishing the standard, the principle adopted was to standardise on whatever helped the manufacturers most.

Each local Esso office has now been given a full description of its country specific solution from the two firms that submitted the lowest prices in a Europe-wide competition. The standard answers are described in a pack that contains the agreed standard layout, a pricing document and the options available. Esso believes it is important to maintain the element of competition in each country by leaving it to its local companies to decide which they use. This provides an incentive for the companies to search with the local Esso staff for improvements.

Each year Esso looks at the average cost of each country's standard service stations and compares it with the last cost for a traditional station. This is used to calculate the total annual saving, which helps identify countries where further improvements can be made.

Then the best ideas from anywhere in Europe are used to help the local staff match the best performance.

managing building projects. Partnering depends on both types of information being taken very seriously and used by managers at all levels to guide continuous improvement.

FINAL WORKSHOP

When the project is finished it is useful to hold a final workshop to evaluate the effectiveness of the

Partnering effort, recognise achievement, and identify lessons learned. The measured benefits provide a reliable basis for the workshop as they provide important evidence about the team's performance.

It is also important to use the final workshop to ensure that the real improvements achieved are captured for future projects. In this way Partnering

Feedback gem – Tarmac uses Feedback to search for better ways of working

The Special Projects Division within Tarmac is responsible for the design and construction of the new PFI funded hospital at Dartford and Gravesham – the work is directed by Peter Couch, a very experienced project manager who has developed a broad understanding of the interactions between medical technology, design concepts, the technology of building structures and services, construction issues, and the PFI.

His approach is shaped by a vision for a new business for Tarmac in the growing PFI and medical facilities markets. Tarmac is bidding for several other PFI hospitals and intends to use the same approach on those it wins.

To ensure that lessons are applied to future projects the team holds annual reviews to measure their own performance. The whole team attends a workshop to identify what has gone wrong, what should have been done better, and lessons for the future. Peter Couch encourages a totally open approach in which no animosity, blame or criticism will be allowed by beginning the workshop with a frank, no punches pulled, discussion of his own failures.

Tarmac is actively encouraging its whole workforce to search for better ways of working. Target 2000 is an annual awards scheme for the best ideas from employees throughout the Tarmac Group. Peter is keen that the Dartford and Gravesham Hospital project will do well in this competition in 1998. He has particularly targeted the award for 'Groupness' which is awarded to the project that uses the largest number of Tarmac Group companies.

A key part of developing the new business is to encourage specialist contractors to invest in training their managers to take more responsibility for inter-face issues. The approach used on the Dartford and Gravesham Hospital project, in which Tarmac manage all the inter-faces, is cautious. In the long run it is likely to be more efficient for the specialists to deal directly with each other. As they build their experience of working together, this will develop naturally and the training is designed to ensure that this really does happen and is effective.

can provide a basis for the continuous improvement on which all really excellent organisations ultimately depend.

TELL SENIOR MANAGEMENT

At the end senior management needs to be informed of the benefits delivered by Partnering and there is no better way to do this than to express them as hard facts that have impacted positively on the bottom line. The feedback to senior management should be illustrated by examples that show how project teams cut out waste and they should also emphasise and describe the benefits for individuals, teams and firms if they continue to be involved in Partnering.

the seven pillars of partnering

A guide to second generation partnering

Project

Checklists

chapter 5

Project Checklists

Second Generation Partnering is applied to projects undertaken within a Strategic Partnering framework. It can also be applied to the 'projects' within one-off mega-projects

Project Partnering is achieved via a core team, usually appointed by the senior managers responsible for the scheme. With Strategic Partnering, project teams are normally appointed by the Strategic Team.

This chapter provides a checklist for core teams of the essential elements of Project Partnering provided when 'The Seven Pillars of Partnering' are all in place. All the elements are necessary for Second Generation Partnering to be truly successful.

With some very experienced Partnering teams all the elements will be in place. For others the pillars have to be built up systematically as people gain greater experience of Partnering. On all except very large projects, it would be very difficult and expensive to attempt to get everything right in a team with little or no previous experience of Partnering. In these circumstances the core team should use First Generation Partnering. On one-off mega-projects the initial workshop should aim at agreeing which pillars will be put in place first. This will largely be determined by where the team see the main challenges or the biggest payoff. Then, as experience of Partnering grows through the project, further progress can be made step by step. A good rule is not to attempt more than one or two major steps forward on any one phase of a mega-project.

CORE TEAMS

Individual projects need to be managed by core teams who work co-operatively. A core team includes all the people able to make a significant contribution to decisions about the design of the building or the management of the project. This changes as the project moves through its key stages. The biggest change occurs as projects move from the initial creative design stage to the implementation stage, when formal planning and control techniques can be used. A typical arrangement may include the following firms:

Initial Creative Design Stage

- Project Manager
- Concept Designer
- Construction Manager
- Specialist Contractors for key elements
- Cost Manager
- Client

Plan and Control Stage

- Project Manager
- Construction Manager
- Design Manager
- Detail Designers
- Site Manager
- Specialist Contractors for key elements
- Cost Manager
- Client

Within the core team, each key aspect of the project is allocated to one person who is responsible for providing leadership. This involves establishing the requirements, expressing these in clear practical targets, ensuring suitable control systems are in place, monitoring progress, making sure problems are dealt with and targets are achieved. An important role of the core team is to set up task forces to deal with each major group of elements and significant aspect of the project. These bring together specialists in the particular work and relevant core team members to find the best possible answer consistent with the project's objectives.

Core teams work through workshops. At the first workshop, the members agree mutual objectives, how decisions will be made and problems will be resolved, and what specific improvements they will make. Follow up workshops take place every month to monitor progress and resolve problems. The final workshop evaluates project performance, discusses problems and defects, and their causes, identifies good ideas that emerged from the project and considers how these contributed to the project's success. The final workshop also feeds back the results to all concerned. Firms are employed on a contractual basis that removes concerns about whether they will get paid. The precise terms depend on the nature of the project. The overall aim is to empower all members to concentrate their efforts on doing their best work for the good of the project.

Core teams seek to drive down costs to the customer and to maintain or increase profits for all the firms involved in their projects.

Everyone in the core team has a joint responsibility for the project. Decision making is open and all members are expected to join in discussions and raise any concerns they have.

Once a decision is made, the whole core team supports it and concentrates on making sure it is put into effect. It is not legitimate to be wise after the event or to say 'I told you this would happen'. Core team members always check work is

A similar process of gradually building up the Pillars has to be employed by Strategic Teams who will set the core team the objective of developing one or two specific Pillars. Then, over a series of projects, they will all be given attention. The project checklists are based on the lessons from the research and are designed to help core teams use Partnering. Each list identifies what needs to be done for Partnering to be fully successful and so by working through the checklists, core teams will be provided with a guide to those features that still need attention.

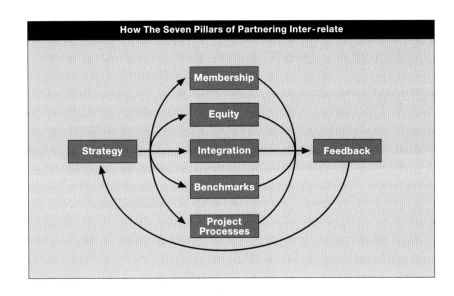

How The Seven Pillars of Partnering Inter-relate

properly completed before moving to the next stage of the process.

In summary core team's ensure that:

- All the individual responsibilities are carried out.
- The client's business case and the needs of the users are satisfied.
- Quality, time and cost targets are met.
- The finished building provides good value.
- Good ideas generated during the project are fed back to all concerned.

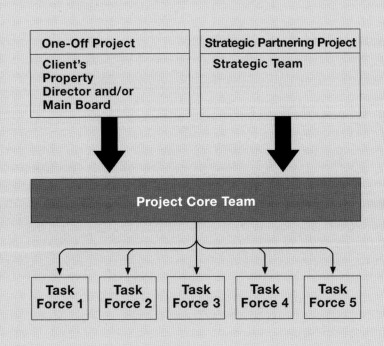

Project Checklists

STRATEGY	DONE?
The core team (with the client) has produced an agreed mission statement describing the challenge or opportunity underlying the project.	✓
The core team has identified all the internal and external stakeholders that influence the client's objectives and considered what each could get from the project that is exciting, surprising and goes beyond their expectations.	✓
The core team help prepare the client's business case or at least discuss it openly at a partnering workshop held early enough for building issues to be taken into account.	✓
The core team members can describe the client's business case in terms that the client understands and agrees with. The client's project manager acts as a gatekeeper providing access for the team to influential people within his or her own organisation; the client's project manager has created a single team approach inside the client's organisation and acts as an internal champion for the project when concerns arise internally.	✓
The core team spend time early in the project identifying risks and opportunities and agreeing how to deal with them.	✓
The core team has produced a written Brief which is as detailed as the client's objectives will allow. The Brief will develop as key decisions are made.	✓
The final Brief sets out clear and agreed objectives for the core team and carefully thought-out requirements for the building. It identifies potential problems and risks and defines the measurements used to evaluate the project's success.	✓
The core team members understand the current Brief, including the client's criteria for success, the standards and targets that must be met and how flexibly they can be interpreted.	✓
The core team members understand the client's priorities and values and have discussed the kind of trade-offs that can be allowed.	✓
The core team has assessed the risk of changes to the client's objectives and taken this into account in its working methods.	✓

MEMBERSHIP	DONE?
The necessary skills are available early so all members of the team, including specialist contractors, have every opportunity to cooperate in making their best possible contribution to the success of the project	✓
For key aspects of the project clusters of firms are appointed that have worked together on earlier projects. As far as possible the people involved have worked with the client on similar projects.	✓
Team members are competent in their own discipline and skilled in communicating their decisions and judgements in terms other disciplines understand.	✓
Team members are selected very carefully to match the needs of the project, especially whether it is intended to deliver routine efficiency or to encourage creativity in a search for new answers.	✓
Firms select people with flexible attitudes and authorise them to adopt new ways of working at three distinct levels: ● **Strategic** – leaders of the core team who determine the overall vision ● **Tactical** – designers and managers who define the building and run the control systems needed to produce it efficiently ● **Operational** – managers responsible for the work of each specialist.	✓
The core team is carefully selected to form a balanced team that includes people who between them provide all the characteristics needed for effective team working.	✓
Training is provided for all who need it in communication skills such as empathetic listening so people become better at understanding and discussing their real feelings about decisions. Training is also available for core skills such as process analysis, work planning, problem solving and performance measurement.	✓
Individuals unable to act cooperatively are replaced. In exceptional cases, special provision is made for an unusually talented person.	✓
Individuals who develop partnering skills are rewarded by their firms.	✓

EQUITY	DONE?
Everyone can concentrate on achieving agreed mutual objectives without having to worry about whether they will get paid.	✓
The mutual objectives ensure that everyone shares rewards and risks without some parties, even if they contribute their best efforts, loosing out relative to the others.	✓
The core team agree a reward structure which provides a realistic chance that the client will pay a fair price and the industry firms will earn a fair profit.	✓
The reward structure provides team incentives where payments to all the firms involved increase directly with their joint success in meeting the client's objectives.	✓
The costs of Partnering (changing established ways of working, training and workshops) are taken into account in agreeing the reward structure.	✓
Incentives for the whole team, including the client, are funded out of savings which come from improving performance and identifying and driving out waste.	✓
Incentives are based on agreed measures of the team's joint performance.	✓
Effective incentives for firms with little experience of Partnering include: ● Repeat business if the project goes well ● Sharing money saved ● Lump sum bonuses for meeting a defined cost or time target.	✓
Effective incentives for firms with some experience of Partnering include: ● Agreeing a fixed price for work based on a careful evaluation of all the risks so as to provide a fair profit ● Profit sharing based on a carefully defined target cost and an openly agreed allocation of profits and losses. Good schemes often allocate a fixed percentage of savings to the firm that had the good idea.	✓
Effective incentives for firms experienced in Partnering usually take the form of: ● Fair open book arrangements guided by tough cost control and random audits in which firms are paid an agreed sum which provides a fair profit and contribution to their fixed overheads plus all their properly incurred costs.	✓
The arrangement agreed for dealing with rewards reflects the form of procurement used, so there are no contradictions.	✓
The contract reflects a cooperative, non-adversarial way of working (research suggests that the New Engineering Contract helps to engender cooperative attitudes).	✓
The client has arranged project-wide professional indemnity so everyone can concentrate on the best interests of the project without having to worry about their own legal positions.	✓

Project Checklists

INTEGRATION	DONE?
Firms and individuals join the project with win/win agreements. If this is not possible they walk away (win/win or no deal).	✓
Firms, especially smaller suppliers, are treated reasonably. Fair payment terms are agreed and honoured.	✓
Firms with little experience of partnering nominate an individual as a single point of responsibility for dealing cooperatively in all external relations with other firms.	✓
People not used to cooperative ways of working are given training in teambuilding skills and coached in understanding cooperation.	✓
Firms use hand picked cooperative people who naturally adopt trusting attitudes.	✓
Senior management in all the firms encourage and support people acting cooperatively. They are open about commercial information. They treat their subordinates exactly as they want their best clients to be treated. They do not hover over, check up on and direct their people. They allow people to judge themselves because this gives a more accurate picture of how they are performing.	✓
Middle managers are open in transferring knowledge between firms and constantly look for organisational or system changes that will link their firms better.	✓
People who carry out basic operational work day-to-day have timely access to the information, resources or people needed to do their best work – irrespective of who owns them.	✓
The client does not impose answers on the rest of the team but joins in open decision making as an equal partner. Frequent meetings are used to keep everyone, especially senior management, informed about progress.	✓
The core team has the authority to accept joint responsibilities and all the formal agreements support this.	✓
The core team has agreed ways of arriving at decisions which include clear problem resolution processes. The team stresses the benefits of cooperation and the punishments for adversarial behaviour.	✓
In making decisions people focus on interests rather than personalities or positions. They put their cards on the table openly. They try to understand each other's point of view and actively look for win/win agreements.	✓
The team makes sure they are successful by reaching agreements that will work as planned every time.	✓
The team has joint social events that build a sense of community and team spirit and helps people understand how to relate to each other.	✓
Trust and cooperative attitudes are build up and sustained at workshops where everyone explains their role and expectations of the project. Senior management reinforces this by talking about the benefits of trusting others and the need to break down prejudicial barriers.	✓
Trust is developed by taking every opportunity for people to work with those they know so they have the confidence to: ● Not promise more than they can deliver and so keep all their commitments ● Get to know others as individuals, understand what motivates them and treat that as important ● Pay attention to the 'kindnesses' and 'courtesies' that build relationships ● Face differences and work at reaching a mutually agreed set of expectations ● Have the integrity that goes beyond honesty by avoiding saying anything that is deceptive or lowers the dignity of others ● Be loyal to and defend those who are absent and so build the trust of those who are present ● Apologise sincerely when they make a mistake of judgement.	✓
Everyone tries to behave cooperatively. They: ● Behave as if other people are trustworthy and continue as long as this cooperative behaviour is returned ● Punish people who behave badly by withdrawing trust This may involve additional checks and controls, tough audit procedures or being thrown off the project ● Forgive adversarial behaviour when others return to cooperation ● Reward cooperation. Be provoked by adversarial behaviour and take time to explain why.	✓
People are rewarded for taking risks to build up trust. They are given feedback from their bosses, peers and subordinates about how their behaviour is perceived.	✓
Communication is faster and it needs fewer inspections and audits, and fewer decision levels.	✓
People respect each other, they enjoy their work and the team talks about and celebrates successes.	✓

BENCHMARKS	DONE?
The project is guided by two or three objective measurements of performance set by the core team.	✓
Measurements should allow projects to be compared. It usually helps if the measurements are expressed as a numerical ratio or percentage.	✓
The benchmarks accurately reflect the client's objectives and concentrate everyone's attention on the important issues.	✓
The benchmarks take account of any Strategic Team policy aimed at continuous improvement over a series of projects.	✓
The benchmarks deal with areas that have a direct positive impact on business success for the firms involved.	✓
The benchmarks focus worker's attention on their own responsibility for the project's success and encourage them to look for ways of improving joint performance.	✓
The benchmarks have been discussed across the whole workforce. Regular reports on progress are produced and publicised within all the firms involved.	✓
When firms have little experience of Partnering, the benchmarks should be those that will show significant benefits quickly. Once Partnering is established, benchmarks can be more subjective and relate to longer-term benefits such as improved ways of working, innovations etc.	✓

Project Checklists

	DONE?
The core team agree the process they are going to use right at the outset of the project. In particular they decide whether they can work through a predetermined process or whether they needed a flexible process defined as the project progresses.	✓
Each activity in the process has been reviewed by answering ten questions: ● What is necessary for it to be carried out efficiently? ● What has to be in place before it can begin? ● Does it add value? ● How could it add more value? ● Is it essential or could it be eliminated? ● How can it be simplified? ● How can it be carried out more efficiently or quicker? ● What are the key issues, problems and risks? ● Can it be carried out in parallel with other activities? ● What determines that it is complete?	✓
The core team agree a reward structure which provides a realistic chance that the client will pay a fair price and the industry firms will earn a fair profit.	✓
The core team aim for repetition within the process because they recognise this can lead to dramatic improvements in productivity.	✓
As far as possible the project team is working through a well established process that has been refined at a strategic level outside of the project. It includes no more than one or two new steps aimed at defined improvements in performance.	✓
The process is planned as far ahead and in as much detail as possible without constraining the core team in its search for the best possible answers.	✓
The agreed process is described in a diagram that shows the actions the core team plans to use to produce the building the client needs. The diagram records the key supply chains and so helps everyone, including specialists and suppliers, understand their responsibilities.	✓
Everyone in the project team fully understands the process they are working through and have bought into it. They have the confidence that if a target changes, the process will be reviewed and, if absolutely necessary, changed.	✓
The project control systems have been designed to support the selected process so the project team work within a fixed budget and handover date using standards and clear procedures in-so-far as the objectives allow.	✓
The core team work through carefully managed meetings and where innovation is needed, they use a project office to work together.	✓
Programme milestones are reliably met. Where innovation is needed, milestones are interpreted flexibly on the basis of providing just sufficient information to avoid delaying the project.	✓
The agreed cost plan is worked to and where innovation is needed, cost control is used to drive a search for savings using open book accounting and tough audit procedures.	✓
Zero defects are aimed at by everyone in the team. Quality control is entrusted to experienced professionals who have a deep understanding of the technologies used.	✓

FEEDBACK	DONE?
Throughout the project feedback is used to look for further improvements in performance. Feedback is never used as a basis for blame or punishment.	✓
Measurements, benchmarked to industry norms, are routinely produced throughout the project to demonstrate the ongoing improvements being achieved and help convince clients and senior management to continue using Partnering.	✓
The improvements should be related to the balance sheet or, even better, the share price of the firms involved.	✓
A final workshop is held to evaluate how effective Partnering has been, recognise achievements, and identify lessons learned.	✓
The project team's success is measured using benchmarks on productivity (cost, schedule and profitability) and process (safety, teamworking, problem resolution and inter-firm improvements).	✓
The Strategic Team and senior management in all the firms involved are informed of the benefits delivered by partnering. Feedback should be expressed in terms of hard facts that impact positively on the bottom line. It should also describe the benefits for individuals, teams and firms if they continue to be involved in Partnering.	✓

the seven pillars of partnering

A guide to second
generation partnering

Third Generation

Partnering

Third Generation Partnering

The industry's leading clients drove the move to Second Generation Partnering and are increasingly setting the pace, so that a Third Generation of partnering is now on the horizon.

Many of the leading clients involved in the case studies see Partnering as the means of helping the industry to modernise itself. These clients have helped identify the way forward for the industry. But once this has been achieved these clients want to concentrate on their core business and 'outsource' construction.

Customers in all industries are demanding more. They want better value based on lower costs and more performance. They want greater certainty, including guarantees and after care. They want faster delivery measured in days and weeks not months and years. They expect zero defects as the norm.

The driving forces behind these new demands are highly competitive global markets, rapidly changing technologies and a growing concern for the quality of all our environments.

The fundamental fact of life is that organisations have to meet the needs of their ultimate customers. For construction these are the users and whoever provides the finance – or an income stream to support the finance. If these two groups do not exist, there is no effective demand for construction.

The key needs in satisfying the demands of today's customers are to provide quality, flexibility and innovation. Firms that meet these needs have moved beyond a narrow focus on productivity to emphasise the need for involvement, innovation and creativity at all levels in the workforce.

Leading firms in both the manufacturing and service industries now work through flexible, intelligent organisations able to gather and analyse data from a wide range of sources, encourage reflection, and translate the results into day-to-day practice. These organisations are informed by strategic research and information, and promote innovation and problem-solving across the whole workforce.

The implications for the building industry are profound. It needs to make three major changes. First it needs to become genuinely market orientated in understanding customers and producing more than just products and services – relationships are seen as vitally important and Partnering meets this new requirement.

Second, the building industry needs to use all the talent locked into its supply chains – the suppliers and specialists that provide the materials, components and systems that make up modern buildings and environments. Partnering first emerged to meet this need in the manufacturing industries and it is ideally suited to helping the building industry develop efficient, innovative supply chains.

Third, the industry needs to build continuous improvement into all its work. The industry's professionals can no longer think in terms of individual projects. They need the support of new systems and processes that will take time to become fully developed and will have an impact across a series of projects rather than an individual project.

Fortunately, Partnering provides the essential elements of what is needed for the building industry to focus on continuous improvement.

As the case studies show, a small elite band of firms have already begun to make the necessary changes. A few have most of the elements in place and these will provide an entirely new approach to building called Third Generation Partnering.

NEW MARKETS

Third Generation Partnering serves markets that are very different from those the traditional construction industry is used to dealing with. IT is driving many of the changes in the ways buildings are being used. In retailing for example, order and collect outlets require very different buildings from today's supermarkets. They will, in turn, change distribution systems leading to new kinds of warehousing and other facilities. Another trend is that many large organisations are fragmenting so that only a core team is left in a London head office and most managers work in smaller, more flexible but widely distributed spaces. This in turn is resulting in a growing demand for high quality serviced offices that provide a full range of modern technology and good staff support – but can be rented by the hour.

These developments are why future buildings must provide greater flexibility.

The rate of change is now such that the industry has to respond by providing environments capable of almost continual change and development. In the short-term the traditional industry may be able to survive by finding uses for old buildings. But in the longer-term the industry will need to change so it can offer customers a range of spaces and quality standards at predetermined prices that provide outstanding value. Some of these new buildings will have a long life because they will adapt to users' changing needs. More specialised buildings will still be individually designed. Many will use standard components that can be reused as the specialised functions change. Others will be concept designs exploring new ideas in style or technology. The results will often be products and services customers have not even dreamt of.

THIRD GENERATION PARTNERING – THE JAPANESE INFLUENCE

Japan's construction industry has used what is now called partnering as its normal way of working for many years.

Partnering is applied because cooperative long-term-relationships are an important feature of Japan's management culture. A contractor would see it as a matter of great dishonour if another contractor ever won work from one of his established customers. Many Japanese contractors use subcontractors that they have worked with for decades; in some cases for more than a century. In all of these relationships there is a relentless search for ways of improving performance.

Continuous improvement applies internally as well as externally because workers have the benefit of life-time employment. This gives them a real interest in the efficiency and success of their firm. An important effect of this is that every work group has regular quality circle meetings to discuss how they can do their work better. This generates many practical ideas about how the product or the process can be improved.

There is little doubt about the benefits. Japan has the most efficient construction industry in the world. Zero defects is a reality for many major customers. Projects finish exactly on time, to the day. Contractors spend a lot of time working with customers to understand their business and to identify and create opportunities where construction will add value to the customer's business. As a result construction demand is three times as high as in the UK. Also demand is much more stable than in the UK because the big contractors have ensured that the Japanese government understands the importance of economic and business stability. As a result the government invests in new public sector construction when private sector demand falls so as to stabilise demand.

In Japan, what we call partnering, has produced a very distinctive way of working. Contract conditions have no effect on the way people work. Everyone is culturally motivated to concentrate on completing each project as efficiently as possible and looking for ways of continuously improving their performance for the future.

Design build is used universally. Japanese contractors will work only from their own drawings. Even if the client employs a design consultant for the concept design, the contractor does all the construction drawings. In producing them, the contractor ensures the details are well within the competence of the specialist contractors and they standardise as much as possible. As a result there tends to be more 'engineering' than 'architecture' in the design of buildings in Japan.

No opportunity to reinforce the importance of safety is missed. For example, at the morning briefing meetings subcontract teams routinely check that the team next to them is wearing all the right safety clothes. Also targets are set for the number of man/days worked without a reportable accident and the current score is displayed prominently on construction sites next to the target.

Construction planning is taken very seriously by Japanese contractors.

The overall programme establishes monthly milestones. Within this, each week's work is planned in detail. All of this is done before work begins on site. Daily work is planned on site to meet the weekly plan. Problems are kept to an absolute minimum by careful and detailed consideration of every aspect.

When the plan is put into effect by the project manager they will have been involved in the design and planning at head office from day one of the project. Once on site they dress in overalls and boots so they can get out and about making sure that everyone knows what work they are supposed to be doing. Japanese management is very much hands-on to ensure that everything is going according to plan.

Projects on site work through a standardised daily routine that begins with exercises to get the body ready for work. Next there is a briefing of the whole workforce by the Project Manager to ensure that everyone knows the overall objectives for the day and the main events that are planned. Then there is a short purposeful meeting for each work team to make sure that everyone understands their own day's work.

Once the team is physically and mentally 'warmed up', everyone concentrates on completing the agreed days work in the day – no matter how long that takes. An important part of the total plan and control system is that every day at 3.00 pm there is a progress and planning meeting attended by the Project Manager's team and the foremen of all the subcontractors working on site. These meetings drive the project forward exactly in accordance with the original plan. There is never any discussion of contractual issues or how people will get paid. There is just a relentless drive to carry out the planned work.

As a result the monthly milestones are always met. Doing so may involve working long hours and working at weekends but by ensuring that the key milestones are never missed, Japanese contractors can be confident in assuring their customers of completion on time.

The important lesson from the Japanese experience is that construction can be managed in an orderly and efficient manner and continuous improvement is achievable when firms use Partnering.

Customers will want the industry to provide warrantees for tenants and funding institutions. Partnering can consistently deliver this – much more so than relying on contractual provisions. Warrantees should provide certainty of whole life costs by guaranteeing energy costs, running costs, cleaning, etc. By having an all in pre-determined annual cost, companies will be able to see their buildings as operating units with a fixed monthly price. This certainty will be backed by substantial companies if they are to have credibility with major clients. Once this happens buildings will be seen as a flexible resource, available as and when they are needed and disposed of when they are no longer required.

Buildings backed by a complete facilities management service will be available to lease or buy.

Customers will need to be confident that the industry is delivering good value buildings. This depends on the industry providing reliable, independent information about the price and performance of competing products and services.

These are the challenges for the building industry of the 21st century. All this may potentially be achieved via Third Generation Partnering.

Third Generation Partnering will not emerge overnight. Second Generation Partnering relationships need to be established as an essential pre-requisite for Third Generation Partnering.

But firms who do achieve it will create new demand – both at home and overseas. Also Third Generation firms will have the capacity to take the initiative in building markets – for example – a contractor could build a chain of supermarkets in Africa and then get Asda, Sainsbury's or Tesco to run them under a Partnering arrangement.

THIRD GENERATION PARTNERING

Third Generation Partnering means construction firms taking full responsibility for producing and marketing products and supporting services. It turns the building process into a cycle of fundamental activities linked by cooperative decision making activities. It uses partnering as the normal way of working in all key relationships. Building industry firms using Third Generation Partnering work as equals in Partnering arrangements with their customers. They know that most customers now face international competition and so their buildings and services must be world-class. They understand also that a decision to buy a new building has to be made in competition with other capital investment decisions. Consequently they concentrate on producing buildings and services that contribute more to the success of customers' businesses than, for example, investing in IT.

Having understood how customers use buildings Third Generation Partnering meets the new demands by mobilising development expertise.

This second main stage of the new building cycle brings together professionals in property management, concept and scheme design, construction management, finance and cost control. Together they become expert at developing products and services aimed at specific market sectors so that construction becomes a series of very distinct industries. Each is made up of clusters of consultants and contractors specialising in the technologies needed to deliver a particular kind of building, product or associated service to meet the needs of the toughest and most demanding customers.

The third fundamental activity is the production of the required building. This is achieved through well-developed supply chains guided by Partnering. By concentrating on specific market sectors, groups of suppliers and specialist contractors provide a key driving force for continuous improvement. They innovate, use R&D and work in many Partnering teams to produce buildings that are genuinely high-tech using advanced manufacturing and assembly technologies.

ACHIEVING THIRD GENERATION PARTNERING

Wide experience in other industries and evidence from world class construction firms suggests that the seven strategic pillars of Partnering identified in Second Generation Partnering are all needed to provide a secure basis for Third Generation Partnering. Otherwise the investments in skills, systems and technologies will be put at risk by the poorly developed relationships which eventually tear the partnering firms apart.

A key part of achieving Third Generation Partnering is the use of strategic task forces to tackle specific long-term improvements to performance. These commonly bring together people drawn from a cluster of specialist firms responsible for an element of the buildings or a specific aspect of the management of projects. They are given time and resources to innovate free from the pressures of individual projects and their work feeds into the mainstream of the industry's work which is in the hands of project core teams.

Within Third Generation Partnering arrangements, the strategic task forces, together with the core teams on individual projects, form what is normally described as middle management.

Project core teams work within the strategic direction provided by top management. Their central task is to define the required product sufficiently to design an appropriate process and then select the right mix of skills, information systems and decision systems to carry out the project. The result of their work provides the design and management framework for first line managers.

The equivalent of first line management is provided by the suppliers and specialist firms that design, manufacture and construct the end product. As well

as producing the building and providing the services required by the customer, Third Generation Partnering requires the specialist firms to continuously improve their own performance within the direction set by the overall strategic objectives. The suppliers and specialist firms that are critical to success in a particular market sector form the supply chains by working with second level specialists in Partnering arrangements and so on – in many cases to a third or even forth level. These clusters of firms often work with several Partnering arrangements in the same or even different market sectors.

The work of all the various firms involved in Third Generation Partnering is guided by a new building cycle. This is illustrated below.

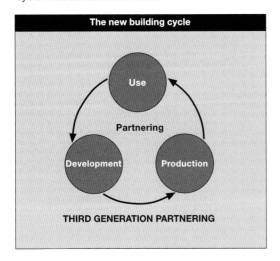

The new building cycle

Partnering

Use

Development   Production

THIRD GENERATION PARTNERING

Each of the elements is crucial to successful building. Partnering is important in all elements but is crucially necessary in the linking activities as these involve intensive joint decision making which defines the work for the next fundamental activity.

Use: involves professionals like facilities managers who understand the customer's business and market, the users' needs and how buildings support them.

Use: Development: involves cooperative working to agree how buildings can support users' work and the customer's business. This results in a brief.

Development: involves professionals in property management, concept and scheme design, construction management, finance and cost management.

Development: Production: involves cooperative working to produce a definition of required building work and the criteria for success. It results in a scheme design, budget and completion date.

Production: involves professionals in detail design, manufacture and construction.

Production: Use: involves cooperative working to agree how the building should be used, run and maintained, including how it can be changed by the

users as their needs alter. This results in the users' manual.

The building cycle is implicit in all the various forms of Third Generation Partnering. It provides an essential basis for the distinctive feature of Third Generation Partnering – the universal use of cooperative methods driven by the industry itself. In a major break with traditional approaches, it is not dependant on initiatives by customers. The industry uses modern marketing techniques to identify or create new demand. Then it is totally professional in meeting these demands. This gives the building industry its best chance of meeting the challenges set by the Latham Report and becoming a profitable, modern industry.

THIRD GENERATION PARTNERING IN PRACTICE

The factors driving these general developments suggest that three distinctly different kinds of firms will emerge to become the major players in the global building industry of the 21st century. They will be very different to any building industry firms that exist today, but for the sake of continuity we have called them:

- Consultants
- Contractors
- Manufacturers

They will work with supply chains of suppliers and specialist contractors to produce buildings and services tailored to the needs of individual customers who increasingly demand greater flexibility, better value and much faster delivery periods.

The three kinds of firms - Consultants, Contractors and Manufacturers have adopted distinct approaches to meeting these tough demands.

CONSULTANTS

Modern buildings and the services associated with them have become very complex, as has their design and production. The design and construction of most important modern buildings already involve the use of many distinct and specialised technologies which require a variety of specialised skills. All building projects have to bring together groupings of specialist firms to provide what individual customers' need. Third Generation Partnering is giving rise to the emergence of a new breed of consultants skilled in enabling such groupings to work at high levels of efficiency.

These key consultants are able to organise different mixes of design and construction management professionals and specialist contractors. Their approach recognises that really original ideas come from interactions between experts, often working in very small specialist firms.

The consultants of the future will meet the needs of their customers by managing networks of firms. Their distinctive strength will be the ability to

Tarmac fully recognises the value of cooperative relationships and it is the company's policy to use Partnering and the principles of Partnering with all our customers and throughout our supply chains.

**Sir Neville Simms,
Chief Executive,
Tarmac plc**

THIRD GENERATION PARTNERING CASE STUDY - TARMAC

Tarmac's Structure

Tarmac is the UK's leading heavy building materials and construction services group and also has major markets overseas. It already displays many of the features that characterise Third Generation Partnering Contractors – from the generation of innovative solutions, through the supply of materials and construction, to the facilities management of completed projects.

With an annual turnover of more than £2.6 billion, Tarmac employs approximately 24,000 people in 30 countries.

The Tarmac Group now operates through two business streams:

● **Heavy Building Materials**
Tarmac is one of the world's largest suppliers of mineral products. It owns substantial aggregate, crushed rock, sand and gravel, asphalt, slag, concrete and cement businesses in the UK and abroad.

● **Construction Services**
Tarmac is now the largest building and civil engineering contractor and multi-disciplinary consultancy operating in the UK market. It also has a growing international portfolio of work, particularly in mainland Europe, South East Asia, and the Caribbean.

Within the two streams are 12 clearly defined, fully accountable Business Groups which are supported by a central Private Finance Unit and other services. Management at all levels is committed to developing and growing strongly differentiated businesses with the ability, when appropriate, to create innovative linkages.

Internal Partnering

Tarmac is using internal partnering to spearhead a drive to Third Generation Partnering targeting key market sectors and developing packages of products and services that are becoming the benchmark for the industry. This strategy involves Partnering with companies in other industries with complimentary skills, customers, construction design consultants and specialist contractors. The strategy involves developing key businesses inside the Tarmac empire where there will be a continuing demand and work. The most obvious of these are in the prisons and hospitals sectors.

Prisons

The £70 million Fazakerley Prison, (below) completed late in 1997, was a joint PFI venture between Tarmac and Group 4 and involved designing, constructing, financing and now managing a 600 place prison for 25 years. Many Tarmac companies partnered on the project and Tarmac products and services were utilised at every opportunity - in total, 17 Tarmac business units were involved. Compared with traditional methods, the project took less than half the usual time, capital cost has been reduced by 35 per cent and operational costs should be between 10 and 14 per cent lower.

Hospitals

The new Dartford and Gravesham hospital (above) illustrates Tarmac's Third Generation Partnering strategy well. The local Health Trust needed a new 400 bed acute hospital and invited bids from PFI organisations to design, construct, equip and then run the hospital for 25 years. Tarmac provided the construction expertise within the winning PFI team – known as The Hospital Company – which also includes firms that specialise in equipping medical facilities, finance and facilities management.

Partnering is encouraged by sharing the benefits of good ideas and using an open book approach to finance and all information. Tarmac's project records are open to all the consultants and specialist contractors. Equally their records are open to Tarmac and provide the basis for calculating project costs. The financial arrangements mean it is extremely unlikely that any claims will be made because everyone has an interest in minimising costs.

The project uses, as far as possible, well established detailed designs. This reduces risks of failures in the finished buildings, speeds up the design process and makes it less likely that construction will be delayed through late information. In addition to normal cost planning, design is guided by a whole-life cost plan produced with the help of experts in hospital operational and maintenance costs.

Tarmac's expertise in hospitals is now gaining recognition. At the Derby Royal Infirmary Tarmac Services Partnership was recently praised by Brian Abell, the Infirmary's Facilities Manager: "Partnering savings at the Derbyshire Royal Infirmary over the last three years have been reinvested and have provided the funding to carry out 350 hip operations and 750 cataract removals. A total of 1100 Derbyshire patients have received a huge quality improvement to their lifestyle which could not have been possible without our Partnering arrangement," he said.

Continuous Improvement

Tarmac is actively encouraging its whole workforce to search for better ways of working. Target 2000 is an annual awards scheme for the best ideas from employees throughout the Tarmac Group. In 1997 the Fazakerley team won the 'Groupness' Award which is awarded to the project that uses the largest number of Tarmac Group companies. The Dartford and Gravesham hospital team are determined to secure the award in 1998.

Third Generation Partnering

integrate teams drawn from diverse backgrounds and still provide reliable and trusted construction services. Thus they bring together teams of designers, managers, manufacturers and constructors to tackle challenging, one-off building projects.

They need highly trained and experienced management skills supported by well developed IT systems to deliver the world class performance.

The consultants of the future will become very sophisticated at using Partnering flexibly as individual circumstances require. All seven pillars of Second Generation Partnering will be in place and fully developed to give these building industry firms the confidence to concentrate on leading project core teams that deliver creativity, innovation and exceptional value.

CONTRACTORS

The forces shaping contractors involved in Third Generation Partnering are similar. However, they are responding to the complexity of modern buildings by bringing many of the design and construction specialisms into the firm, often by acquisition, and by the strategic management of their supply chains. They offer customers an unambiguous single point of responsibility for delivering packages of buildings and services. Contractors of the future will have the capacity to tackle a wide range of building and other construction work and will usually operate internationally in order to maintain reasonably stable workloads.

Contractors are already developing and growing by working with major customers in Second Generation Partnering arrangements.

The PFI is also helping the new generation of contractors to develop. These projects give responsibility for the building and its operation to the bidding consortia and often the contractors

takes responsibility for shaping the design, construction and facilities management decisions.

Contractors of the future will invest in their supply chains by setting up strategic Partnering arrangements with specialist consultants and contractors to provide skills and knowledge not available in-house. Initially they work at developing these relationships to achieve the full value adding capacity of Second Generation Partnering. In doing this they organise their supply chain relationships in levels. The most important specialists provide a first level that the contractors develop by using strategic partnering. The first level consists of broadly based firms taking responsibility for major groups of elements or services e.g. groundworks, structures, cladding, services, fitting out, technical design, finance, facilities management, etc. The first level firms organise groups of second level specialists who in turn organise third level specialists. Each level provides more specific specialised knowledge and skills. In Third Generation Partnering, this structure is relatively permanent at the strategic level but is used flexibly to suit the needs of individual projects. This enables contractors to resolve the tensions between efficient production and creative design to provide value for their customers.

Future project teams will combine in-house and external people to match the needs of individual customers. They will work through well developed decision making systems and processes that have been developed and honed in Partnering with customers, consultants and specialist contractors and so are inherently efficient. Thus modern contractors will share many of the characteristics of the major car manufacturers in coordinating complex structures of suppliers to deliver customers with committed single point responsibility.

THIRD GENERATION PARTNERING CASE STUDY – GENERAL ELECTRIC CAPITAL MODULAR STRUCTURES

General Electric is a global company with many divisions, one of which is responsible for modular buildings. This part of General Electric's business began in the 1970s in the USA. In 1993 General Electric came to Europe through the acquisition of a trailer rental company in the UK as part of a larger purchase. This provoked a careful look at the European market. As a result GE expanded by buying a Belgium modular building company that it renamed as General Electric Capital Modular Space (GECMS), to form its European modular building division. GECMS has expanded into France and Germany through internal growth and further acquisitions. An indication of the growth is that in 1993 it manufactured about 1,000 units and by 1997, it produced more than 10,000. GECMS aims to have the manufacturing capacity to supply, at competitive prices, throughout Europe within two years.

GECMS regard buildings as commodities delivered when and where customers need them on whatever terms make the best commercial sense to both parties. GECMS' corporate staff are housed in Antwerp and its factory is in Beringen, Belgium. GECMS manufacture and sell or lease complete buildings. They subcontract the non-modular elements. Modular methods are suitable for schools, hospitals, offices, hotels, etc. They are also widely used to provide toilet blocks and project offices.

The market demands two distinct kinds of building. At the higher end modules have a 'traditional' exterior constructed on site. At the lower end buildings are provided complete with a factory fitted exterior.

GECMS can supply a 'traditional' exterior building ready for occupancy eight weeks after it is ordered. If a standard off-the-shelf module is acceptable, it can be ready the day after it is ordered. Modules will be bought back or leases ended when a user no longer needs the building. So customers can have a building for any time frame, from two weeks to 20 years or more.

GECMS' normal terms for a purpose built building provide three interim payments:
● at the start of production
● when the modules are transported to site
● on completion.

Design

GECMS design the modules in-house using a design group led by engineers. They buy architectural advice as and when a particular project requires it.

Manufacture

The factory in Beringen employs about 50 workers who make between 40 and 50 modules a week. A typical module is 20m².

The manufacturing process is a combination of assembling standard industrialised components and traditional craft work. It is organised as several parallel production lines in which modules are moved on wheels along a rail by fork lift trucks. The rails are at ground level and run the length of the factory. Modules are lifted from line to line by two fork lift trucks. There is clearly more scope for automating the manufacturing process in the future.

GECMS subcontracts the manufacture of the components it uses such as floor units, roof units and columns – which are standard – and external walls, including doors and windows and internal partitions – for which there are options. GECMS has two suppliers for each kind of component and works with them on a Partnering basis to look for continuous improvement in costs and performance, including aesthetic appearance. The manufacture of components is generally more automated that GECMS' own process.

Deliveries are organised on something close to a just-in-time basis. Batches are called up as they are needed. This allows the suppliers to manufacture when it suits them and they store sufficient components to meet GECMS' needs. Suppliers tend to be geographically close to the factories and so deliveries can be called up at very short notice.

GECMS buys in floor coverings, roof coverings, sanitary fittings, radiators, pipes and electrical fittings as they are needed and this accounts for about 50% of the cost of a completed building. Design, manufacturing, delivery and construction on site make up the rest.

Construction

GECMS has its own directly employed workforce for site construction in the countries at the centre of Europe but uses subcontractors elsewhere.

Quality

A tough supplier quality control system is employed that aims at no more than one defect per million parts. GECMS takes Total Quality Management (TQM) seriously by having a continuing programme of improvement projects. In these a person, called a black belt, is given about six specific improvements to achieve – for example – reduce complaints from customers about errors in billing. This is usually a two year full-time assignment. The black belt's responsibility for each specific improvement begins with forming a task force of the people who will need to be involved in making the improvement. Then he or she leads the task force in defining the required improvement, investigating the sources of weaknesses, planning how the improvement can be achieved, if necessary arranging training for the people involved and then implementing the planned actions. The results are measured over time to ensure that a real improvement has been achieved.

Third Generation Partnering

MANUFACTURERS

Manufacturers are perhaps showing the greatest progress towards Third Generation Partnering as they can use industrialised technologies to alter the nature of buildings and the way they are produced.

The most important developments are emerging from work with major international customers using partnering to supply prefabricated elements or even whole buildings. At present much of the technology has its origins in British firms but the development of integrated organisations to exploit it is limited in the UK. A few leading foreign owned manufacturers are now operating across Europe and in at least one case, world-wide.

These leading manufacturers set up strategic Partnering arrangements with regional suppliers of the components and elements of their buildings. These firms deliver comprehensive services in support of their products; which are arguably the first ever genuinely industrialised buildings. In the long-term they will market brand named buildings that will provide the houses, offices, shops, factories and utility buildings of the future. They will offer basic buildings and a range of optional extras that give customers real choices about standards and value. Customers will also be offered a choice of financing and after sales care packages. The buildings will be backed by guarantees covering at least ten years maintenance.

At present the manufacturing technology consists of little more than organising traditional crafts in factories. This limits the buildings produced to fairly small standardised ranges. However, the pace of change is accelerating and leading firms will soon be using more progressive and flexible

manufacturing technologies. This will allow manufacturers to have standardised production processes, yet provide much greater variety. In this way they will be able to meet the needs of many customers, more reliably and with greater efficiency than traditional methods have ever achieved.

SUPPLIERS AND SPECIALIST CONTRACTORS

Working alongside the Consultants, Contractors and Manufacturers will be an army of suppliers and specialist contractors. They are essential in developing the new building technologies that Third Generation Partnering is designed for.

The research has identified numerous examples of major companies able to play this key role. They have well-founded R&D capabilities, access to long-term finance and experienced designers that provide a huge potential for new ideas and innovation. This remains largely untapped and frustrated because most of the industry's professionals have failed to engage suppliers and specialist contractors in a serious search for continuous improvement.

By working closely with user and development teams in Third Generation Partnering suppliers and specialists can focus on continuously improving the components and systems that will form buildings for the 21st century. The link formed in this way between production and use is crucial in driving the building cycle to ever higher levels of customer satisfaction. This is exactly what will determine the future health of the UK building industry – satisfied customers.

the seven pillars of partnering

A guide to second generation partnering

Contractual and

Legal Issues

Contractual & Legal Issues

Firms involved in Partnering build their relationships based on trust and cooperation, so there should seldom be a need to resort to the law. However, the very process of Partnering does raise certain legal and contractual issues and there have been some recent developments that it is important to be mindful of. These are summarised here.

THE ARBITRATION ACT 1996 AND THE HOUSING GRANTS CONSTRUCTION AND REGENERATION ACT 1996 (THE CONSTRUCTION ACT)

The new Arbitration Act is aimed at producing quicker, cheaper and much less adversarial justice. However firms who include an arbitration clause must remember that this is binding and they cannot then go back to the Courts later on to try to resolve a dispute. Another important point to remember is that disputes on construction projects often involve a number of parties and the linking of these disputes in arbitration is only possible if all the parties agree. Where this is not forthcoming there is the potential for several 'linked' disputes to be resolved by separate sets of arbitration. In these cases there could be 'inconsistent' findings of fact, which could cause problems.

The Construction Act adjudication provisions require a quick tempo to the process of resolving disputes – typically no more than six to eight weeks from start to finish. There is now some concern in the industry that complex disputes simply cannot be determined this quickly and there are increasing calls for adjudicators to have the discretion (within limits) to extend this period. Some anxieties have also been raised about enforcing the decisions of adjudicators.

Imagine the following scenario:

- The contact has an arbitration clause that forbids arbitration until after completion;
- there is a dispute early in the project;
- one party refers it to adjudication and there is a decision;
- the other party refuses to pay, claiming that there is a further dispute;
- the beneficiary issues a High Court Writ, but this is stayed.

There is no Summary Judgement, therefore, and the whole adjudication process is undermined.

There are, however, ways around the problem:

- The parties should consider the drafting of any arbitration clause carefully. They can decide that the ambit of their clause will not cover an award by an adjudicator.

- An arbitrator may be able to use new powers in the 1996 act.
- Section 39, to make Provisional Orders;
- Section 47, to make Split Orders.
- More drastically (particularly considering the anticipated improvements in the Arbitration Act) the parties may consider excluding an arbitration agreement from their contract.

COMPETITION LAW

A new Competition Bill is expected to become law in July 1998, though it won't become fully effective until 2000.

The Bill addresses the abuse of a dominant position in the market and confers powers on the Director of the Office of Fair Trading to conduct investigations in connection with Article 85 and 86 of the Treaty of Rome (restriction or distortion of competition and abuse of dominant position). It also replaces certain parts of the Restrictive Trade Practices Acts.

Firms involved in Partnering are unlikely to be affected but should be aware that Section 18 prohibits conduct if it consists of:-

- directly or indirectly imposing unfair purchase or selling prices or other unfair trading conditions.
- limiting production, markets or technical development to the prejudice of consumers;
- applying dissimilar conditions to equivalent transactions with other trading parties, thereby placing them at a competitive disadvantage;
- making the conclusion of contracts subject to acceptance by the other parties of supplementary obligations which, by their nature or according to commercial usage have no connection with the subject of such contents.

Under the new Bill the Director of the Office of Fair Trading will be able to conduct investigations, enter premises and seize documents, and can apply to the Court for Enforcement Notices to impose penalties.

EC LAW DEVELOPMENTS

In November 1997 the European Commission published a Notice that more clearly defined what constituted unfair competition.

Readers of *Trusting the Team* may remember the distinction between 'horizontal agreements' (agreements between entities in the same or similar economic position) and 'vertical agreements' (agreements between entities at different positions in the hierarchy of economic activity). Vertical agreements could include a partnering arrangement. The Notice determines once and for all that agreements between undertakings engaged in the provision of services in a 'vertical agreement' do not fall under the prohibition in Article 85(l) of the Treaty of Rome if the aggregate market shares held by all of the participating undertakings do not exceed 10% of the relevant markets (i.e. both product and geographic).

The Commission has also recently published a paper on *The Competitiveness of the Construction Industry*. This recommends increased team working and cooperation and advocates a climate of shared risk and reward.

It concludes by recommending that the construction industry might benefit from emulating the approaches adopted by other industries, where it is more common for designers, contractors, component manufacturers, and sometimes customers to develop new technologies and new models in collaboration. The Report also acknowledges that its recommendations should also apply to the related supply chains and it endorses the use of benchmarking techniques.

TUPE

TUPE will seldom apply to partnering organisations as staff are not normally transferred. However, those involved in establishing new joint businesses or new 'umbrella' organisations should be careful – especially if they plan to formally employ any of their former staff via this new body.

Based on this review of recent legal developments it is clear that partnering presents no insurmountable legal hurdles. Indeed there is no reason why a partnering agreement in the form of a non-legally enforceable Partnering Charter cannot work alongside a traditional contract such as JCT 80.

WHICH CONTRACT TO CHOOSE?

The objectives of Partnering are to:-

- Introduce incentives for performance related activity
- to better define risk and its allocation
- to promote non-adversarial relationships, and
- to develop improvements in performance and its measurability

In such situations procurement routes such as Cost Plus or Construction Management may be more appropriate. The New Engineering Contract (NEC) Second Edition has also found favour with a number of clients looking for a less adversarial relationship with their contractor. This document is strong on the management of activities and interaction but is weak on rights and obligations. Although the NEC sits comfortably alongside the aims of partnering this form of contract may lose its appeal if the parties are forced back to a clear definition of legal rights and obligations. If the NEC or for that matter any standard form is amended, then it loses its appeal as a model for certainty. A contract should define the parties' legal rights and obligations, and users of a contract that avoids such disciplines should be wary in case there is a later breakdown of relationships.

Whatever form of contract is used there should be some regard to amending provisions in the underlying contract so that it dovetails with, at the very least, the disputes resolution clause. If a form of contract is in use with incentive targets involving prime cost and a Guaranteed Maximum Price then the contract should clearly define prime cost and allow for circumstances where the GMP may need adjusting. A more radical approach is sometimes taken by advocating removal from contracts underlying partnering agreements, liquidated damage clauses, defects liability periods and retentions. In the oil and gas sector such drastic measures are sometimes adopted.

Such deletions must however, be made with great care.

LIQUIDATED DAMAGES

These act as a cap on the contractor's liability for delay and on the employer's side massive trust in the contractor's performance must be displayed.

A more pragmatic approach to the imposition of damages is preferable by, for example, introducing grace periods, bonuses and setting damage off against cost savings.

RETENTIONS

In a strategic partnering arrangement with a continuing work load for the contractor then an employer may take a more relaxed attitude to retentions, providing the Employer is satisfied that there is no risk of contractor insolvency.

DEFECTS LIABILITY

One of the objects of partnering is to produce defects free projects, but in the event of breakdown of relationships the employer will have no legal recourse against the contractor.

INSURANCE MARKET

Both the professional indemnity and latent defects insurance markets are appearing slow to recognise the benefits of partnering. Underwriters do not seem to believe that partnering techniques can actually reduce the risk for their professional members. They seem more concerned with the blurring of the edges of responsibility. While they are happy to encourage their members to enter into the spirit of partnering arrangements they insist quite rightly that this should not in any way reduce their legal rights. Part of this legal certainty also requires professional consultants to continue to be obliged to offer collateral warranties to funders and prospective purchasers and tenants of developments. Warranties will remain as part of the underlying contractional framework in defining the ultimate legal responsibilities of the parties and cannot be abandoned by the ever increasing sophistication of partnering techniques. On the other hand the latent defects market is probably beginning to recognise that any collaboration between the consultants and buildability experts should reduce risks, and they are of course comforted by the fact that their monitoring agent should be fully alert to design innovation, and the introduction of technological change - which in the past has caused so many buildings to fail.

Now that Partnering has been practiced for several years there appears to be a growing acceptance of its merits and certainly few contractual or legal reasons why it should not be more widely embraced in the future.

Axelrod R (1984), **The Evolution of Cooperation**; Basic Books

This book provides remarkable evidence from a rich variety of real life situations about the benefits of cooperation. Its great insight is that many situations can be modelled as a game called the Prisoner's Dilemma. The game creates a dilemma by arranging for the players to be jointly better off if they both cooperate but allowing one of them to be even better off if he seeks his own advantage. However, this advantage is at the expense of the other party. The game often results in both parties becoming locked in adversarial competition and the pattern of payoffs means both are worse off.

Belbin R M (1981), **Management Teams**; Heinmann

Belbin has made a long study of the mix of characteristics in teams. An early discovery was that a team composed of the brightest people did not produce the best performance.

He identified a list of the eight roles that are essential for a fully effective team. The full set is most important where change is involved and so is very important in Partnering teams.

Bennett J and Jayes S L (1995), with Reading Construction Forum Partnering Task Force, **Trusting the Team**; Centre for Strategic Studies in Construction

'Trusting the Team' provides a strategic description of Partnering and sets out the business case for using it in all key relationships.

'Trusting the Team' describes Partnering as having three essential features. The first is that partnering teams must agree mutual objectives. The second is to agree how problems will be resolved. The third is that the partnering team actively seek to achieve continuous improvements in their performance.

Bennett J, Pothecary E and Robinson G (1996), with The University of Reading Design and Build Forum, **Designing and Building a World-Class Industry**; Centre for Strategic Studies in Construction

The report is based on extensive research into design-build customers, projects and construction firms and on a vision formed by the Design and Build Forum. It provides an action plan for design build to make the changes needed to deliver both mainstream and new-stream buildings to international standards. It provided the blueprint for setting up the Design Build Foundation. Throughout its recommendations the use of Partnering is explicitly assumed as the basis of all relationships with customers and suppliers.

Carlisle J A (1991), **Cooperation Works...... But is Hard Work! The fundamental cooperative relationship – buyer and suppliers;** John Carlisle Partnership

This paper starts by focusing on fulfilling consumers' expectations. It then looks at the cost of coercion and conflict, and draws on a number of case studies which emphasise the need to ensure that suppliers are confident enough to invest so that customers can have confidence in the goods received. The rewards of successful relationship management are then discussed. A further important message is that good internal communications lead to good external relationships.

Carlisle J A and Parker RC (1989), **Beyond Negotiation; Redeeming Customer-Supplier Relationships**; Wiley

The book is about customer:supplier relationships but the philosophy described applies to any relationship. Indeed much of the evidence provided to support the approach being advocated comes from research into human relationships. The essential idea is that cooperation between contracting parties is a far more powerful strategy for making both parties more profitable than any adversarial approach yet devised. This idea is applied to supply chains to provide practical guidance on effective behaviour in commercial relationships.

Construction Industry Board (CIB) Working Group 12 (1997), **Partnering in the Team**; Telford

The report echoes 'Trusting the Team' in taking the view that partnering's fundamental components are formalised mutual objectives, agreed problem resolution methods, and an active search for continuous measurable improvements.

CIB WG 12 suggests that Partnering is only appropriate between organisations whose top management share the fundamental belief that people are honest, want to do things which are valued, and are motivated by challenge. Such organisations trust their people and seek ways to enable them to add value to their businesses.

The report concludes that Partnering succeeds best, and provides the greatest return on the initial investment of resources, where:

- *the project or programme is high value and risk to the client*
- *it offers contractors the prospect of a large contribution to their turnover together with secure profits*

This report draws extensively and freely on the Partnering literature and rather than make repeated references to key texts, the contribution of the following is fully acknowledged.

Covey S R (1989), **The Seven Habits of Highly Effective People**; Simon & Schuster

This book draws on basic principles of human behaviour in identifying the seven habits adopted by successful people. The seven habits guide people from the childhood state of dependence, first to independence and then to the complete maturity of interdependence. Interdependence leads to higher levels of success and personal happiness. This view is fundamentally important to understanding why Partnering is a more effective way of conducting business than the competitive pursuit of individual interests.

European Construction Institute (ECI) (1997), **Partnering in the Public Sector**; ECI

ECI describes the forms of Partnering that meet the requirements of the European Union's public procurement requirements and the compulsory competitive tendering imposed by the various UK local government acts.

The approach it recommends is post-award project-specific Partnering. Given this ECI consider that Partnering will usually be initiated by the client. It emphasises the importance of commitment at the most senior levels and the need to appoint champions – sentinels of the process – at key points throughout the client's organisation.

The report also describes a toolkit of practical techniques to help apply Partnering at each stage of the project process. This is illustrated by case studies of successful practice.

Fisher R and Ury W (1981), **Getting to Yes**; Hutchinson

This book describes research which shows that successful negotiators behave differently from people who have difficulties in negotiating good agreements. It embodies the behaviour of successful negotiators in just four principles:

- *separate people issues from the subject of the negotiation,*
- *focus on interests not predetermined positions,*
- *generate a range of options,*
- *use objective criteria to value variables.*

John Carlisle Partnership (1991), **Cooperation and Beyond**; John Carlisle Partnership

This manual incorporates the ideas of Axelrod, highlighting the behaviours needed to initiate and sustain cooperation and reinforce the concept of achieving win:win or no deal. The manual highlights the need for creating quality business relationships. Furthermore it recognises that the hierarchical way of thinking does not place enough focus on customers – instead there is still too much emphasis on keeping executives and shareholders happy.

Kanter R M (1989), **When Giants Learn to Dance**; Simon & Schuster

This book describes the changes that are being forced on the USA by competition from Japan. It recognises that the heady days of spending anything to get innovation must give way to cost effective production. Entrepreneurial creativity has to be married to self-disciplined cooperation in multi-firm teams. Relationships and communication and the flexibility to combine units in different ways are more important than formal management structures. Adversarial modes of dealing with outsiders have to be replaced by pooling resources with others, forming alliances to exploit opportunities and linking systems by strategic partnering. The book provides an excellent description of the difficulties of introducing partnering and of the methods used to overcome the barriers.

Lamming R (1993), **Beyond Partnership: Strategies for Innovation and Lean Supply**; Prentice Hall

Lamming's work in the area of organisational relationships is notable in that he has charted the development of partnering in the automotive industry to what he now calls 'lean supply'. Lamming's theory of lean supply illustrates partnering as the first step towards strategically re-engineering the value chain, thereby transforming traditional customer-supplier relationships. His studies conclude that partnering remains constrained in what it can achieve. However, lean supply, the successor of partnering, demands integration as equals.

Pickrell S, Garnett N and Baldwin J (1997), **Measuring Up : A practical guide to benchmarking in construction**; BRE

This report provides a practical guide to using Benchmarking in construction. It uses a seven step model to describe how Benchmarking provides a structured approach to improving performance. The guidance is supported by case studies of Benchmarking in the construction and other industries.

The report is based on research by The University of Reading and BRE guided by a team of industry partners. It was supported by DoE and EPSRC and is designed to provide a standard for applying Benchmarking in the UK construction industry.